W9-API-776

SADLIER PHONICS

Level A

Lesley Mandel Morrow
Senior Author

Marie Garman   **Patricia Maureen Mount**   **Patricia Scanlon**

~~~~ **Literacy Consultants** ~~~~

Heather K. Casey, Ph.D.
Department of Teacher Education
Rider University

Ernest Morrell, Ph.D.
Graduate School of Education
University of California, Los Angeles

Jennifer Rowsell, Ph.D.
Graduate School of Education
Rutgers University

Erica C. Boling, Ph.D.
Graduate School of Education
Rutgers University

Robert Calfee, Ph.D.
Graduate School of Education
University of California, Riverside

Robert Rueda, Ph.D.
Rossier School of Education
University of Southern California

Carmelita Williams, Ed.D.
Graduate School of Education
Norfolk State University

Cheryl Dyer
Assistant Superintendent
Bridgewater-Raritan (NJ) School District

Eleanor M. Vargas
Teacher Education Department
Claremont Graduate University

Diane H. Tracey, Ed.D.
College of Education
Kean University

D. Ray Reutzel, Ph.D.
Emma Eccles Jones College of Education
and Human Services
Utah State University

Printed in the United States of America   ISBN: 978-0-8215-7901-5   18 19 WEBC 22 21 20 19

Contents

★ **Essential Skill**

★ Essential Skill

★ Essential Skill

PARADES

I like to see parades
with the marching bands
and big bass drums;
They make me want to dance
and clap my hands.

People ride in convertible cars
and smile and wave at you
and clowns come down the street
and make you laugh.

A parade makes everybody happy;
people talk and dance and sing—
I like to watch parades
more than any other thing.

Karama Fufuka

Oral Language Why do people have parades?
What other kinds of celebrations are fun?

Name _____

Dear Family,

In this unit about celebrations, your child will review the sounds of the consonant letters. As your child progresses through this unit, you may wish to try these activities together at home.

Apreciada Familia:

Esta unidad es sobre las celebraciones. Los niños aprenderán el sonido de las consonantes. A medida que se avanza en la unidad, pueden hacer estas actividades juntos.

- The consonant letters of the alphabet are shown above. Help your child find the consonants in his or her name.

- Read the poem "Parades" on the reverse side of this page.

- Help your child identify some of the consonants in the poem.

- With your child, think of words that rhyme with **band** and **sing. (hand/land/sand, bing/ding/king/ping/ring/wing)**

- Arriba se muestran las consonantes. Ayude a su hijo a encontrar las consonantes en su nombre.

- Lea el poema "Parades" en la página 5.

- Ayude a su hijo a identificar las consonantes en el poema.

- Juntos piensen en palabras que rimen con **band** y **sing. (hand/land/sand, bing/ding/king/ ping/ring/wing)**

PROJECT

What kinds of celebrations are special for your family? Look at a calendar together and mark the dates of a few of them. Talk about why these days are important. How does your family celebrate them? Help your child find and name some consonants in the names of these celebrations.

PROYECTO

¿ Qué celebraciones son especiales en su familia? Juntos marquen en un calendario las fechas de algunas de ellas. Hablen sobre esos días importantes. ¿Cómo celebra su familia esos días? Ayude a su hijo a encontrar algunas consonantes en los nombres de esas celebraciones.

Ff

Fair starts with the sound of **f.**
Listen for the sound of **f** in the rhyme.

Follow me to the fair,
be the very first one there!
Find your favorite foods to eat,
or find a funny clown to meet!

⭐ **Say** the name of the picture. **Print f** on the line if the picture name begins with the sound of **f.** Then **trace** the whole word.

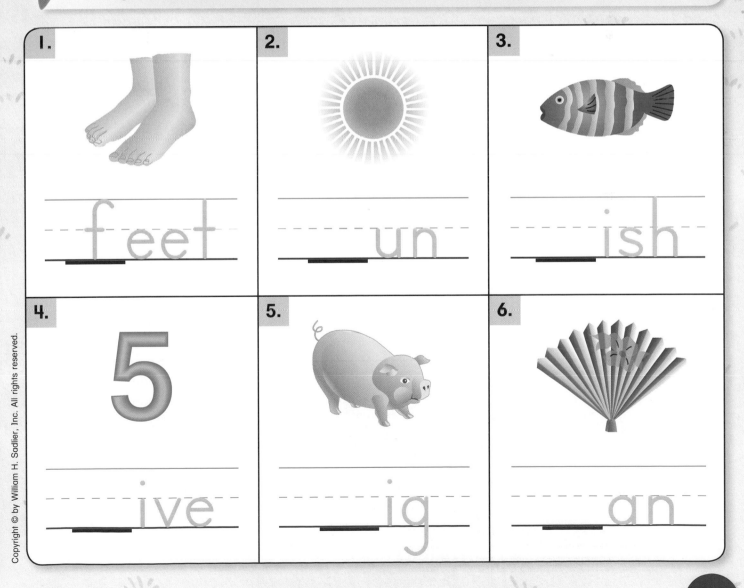

1.

feet

2.

___un

3.

___ish

4.

___ive

5.

___ig

6.

___an

Mm

Moon starts with the sound of **m**.
Listen for the sound of **m** in the rhyme.

One Monday in May,
Mr. Owl played a tune
while little mice danced
beneath the full moon.

Say the name of the picture. **Print m** on the line if the picture name begins with the sound of **m.**

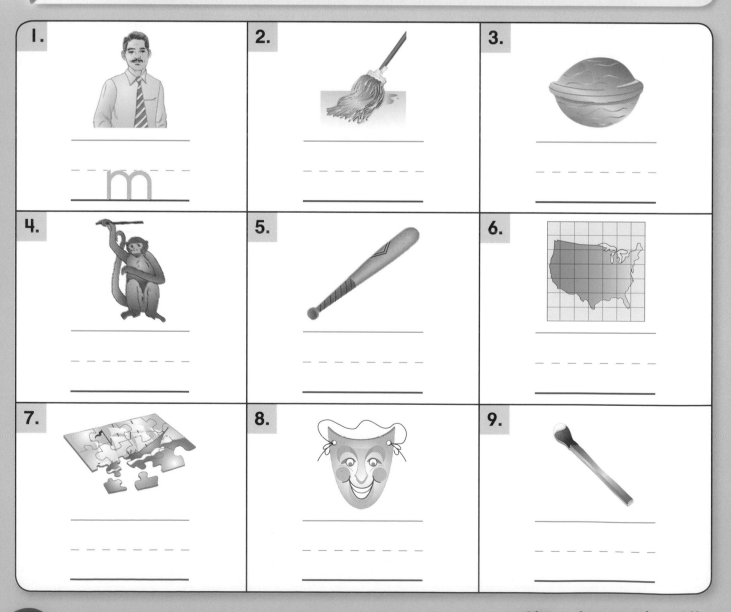

1.

m

2.

3.

4.

5.

6.

7.

8.

9.

Lesson 3 • Phonemic Awareness
Connecting Sound to Symbol: Initial /m/ m

Sing a song with your child
that has an **m** word in it, such
as *Mary Had a Little Lamb.*

Sing starts with the sound of **s.**
Listen for the sound of **s** in the tongue twister.

See Sally and her sister Suzy
sing seven silly songs.

Say the name of each picture. **Circle** the picture whose name
begins with the sound of **s. Print s** on the line.

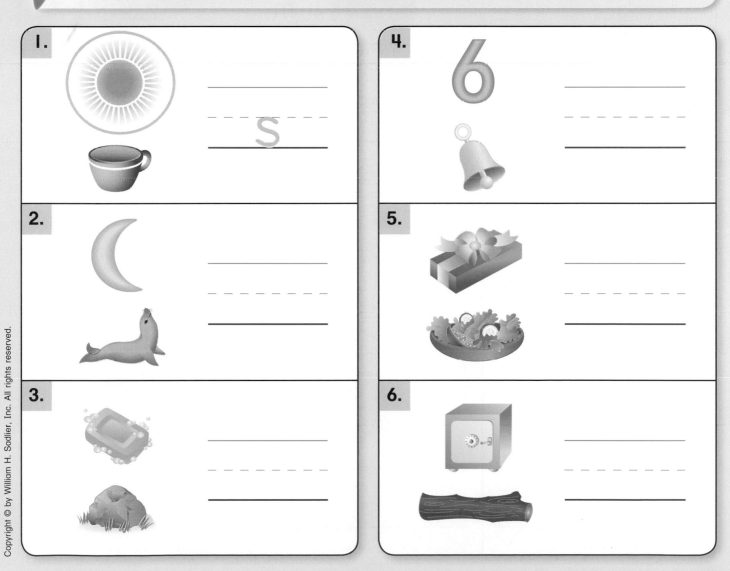

I.
                S

2.

3.

4.

5.

6.

Say the name of the picture. **Circle** the letter that stands for the ending sound. **Print** the letter on the line. Then **trace** the whole word.

1.
f
(m)

gu___

2.
f
s

hoo___

3.
m
f

swi___

4.
s
f

roo___

5.
s
m

dru___

6.
d
f

li___

7.
f
s

el___

8.
s
f

bu___

9.
s
m

broo___

10.
s
m

ga___

11.
f
s

lea___

12.
f
m

ja___

PHONICS ALIVE AT HOME Help your child cut out the pictures. Sort them into groups that end with the sound of **f**, **m**, and **s**.

Ten starts with the sound of **t**.
Listen for the sound of **t** in the rhyme.

Today is my birthday.
It's Tammy's birthday, too.
Today we turn ten.
How old are you?

Say the name of the picture. **Print t** on the line if the picture name begins with the sound of **t.** Then **trace** the whole word.

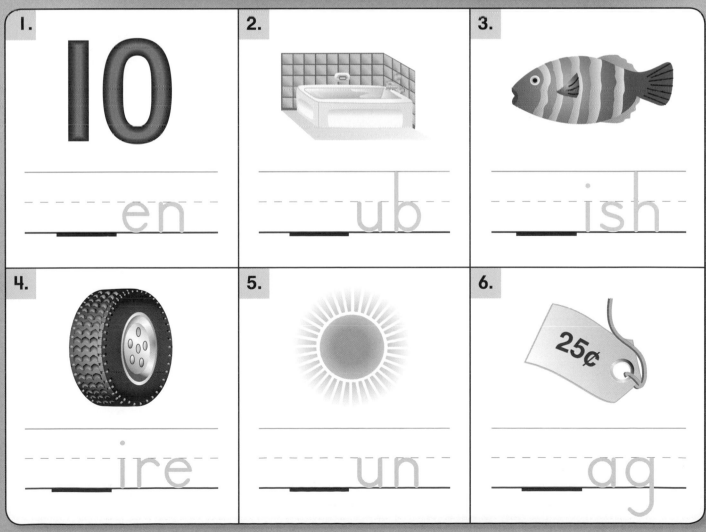

1. ____en

2. ____ub

3. ____ish

4. ____ire

5. ____un

6. ____ag

Hh

Horn starts with the sound of **h.**
Listen for the sound of **h** in the rhyme.

Honk your horn
and shout, "Hooray!"
Have a happy holiday.

Say the name of the picture. **Print h** on the line if the picture name begins with the sound of **h.**

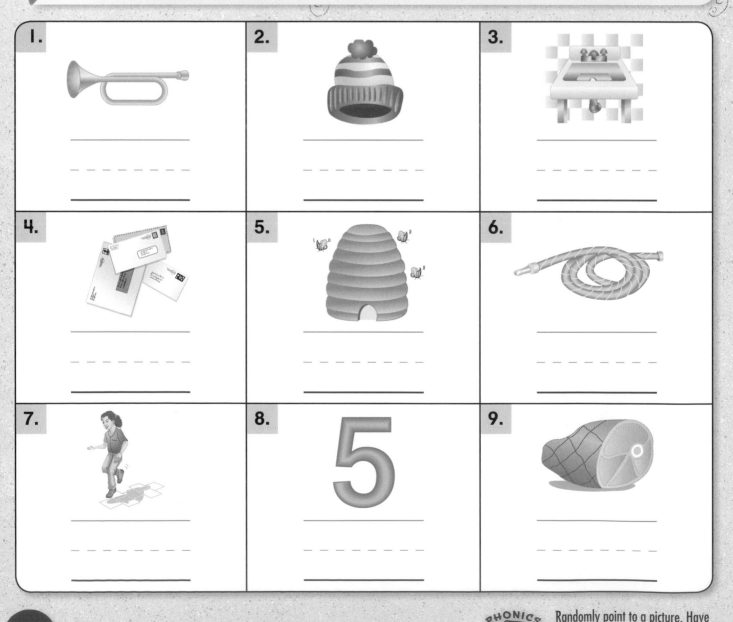

1.

2.

3.

4.

5.

6.

7.

8.

9.

PHONICS
ALIVE AT HOME

Randomly point to a picture. Have
your child give you a high five if its
name begins with the sound of **h.**

Baby starts with the sound of **b.**
Listen for the sound of **b** in the tongue twister.

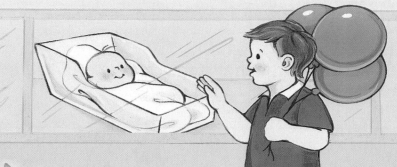

Bobby Baxter bought a
bunch of blue balloons
for his baby brother.

Say the name of each picture. **Circle** the picture whose name
begins with the sound of **b. Print b** on the line.

1.

2.

3.

4.

5.

6.

Say the name of the picture. **Circle** the letter that stands for the ending sound. **Print** the letter on the line. Then **trace** the whole word.

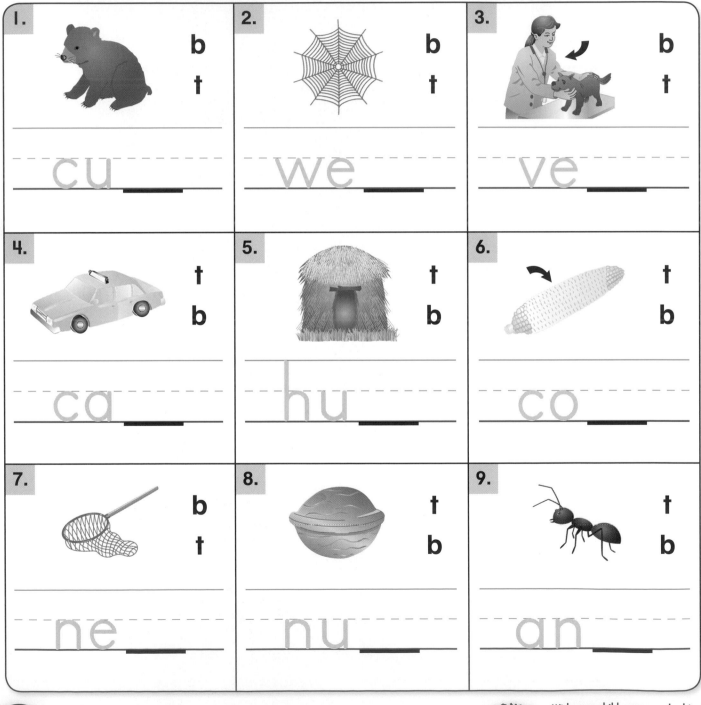

1.	b / t	cu___
2.	b / t	we___
3.	b / t	ve___
4.	t / b	ca___
5.	t / b	hu___
6.	t / b	co___
7.	b / t	ne___
8.	t / b	nu___
9.	t / b	an___

With your child, name each object on this page, stressing the end sound: net-t-t-t; cub-b-b-b.

Check-Up **Say** the name of the picture. **Circle** the letter that stands for the missing sound. **Print** the letter on the line. Then **trace** the whole word.

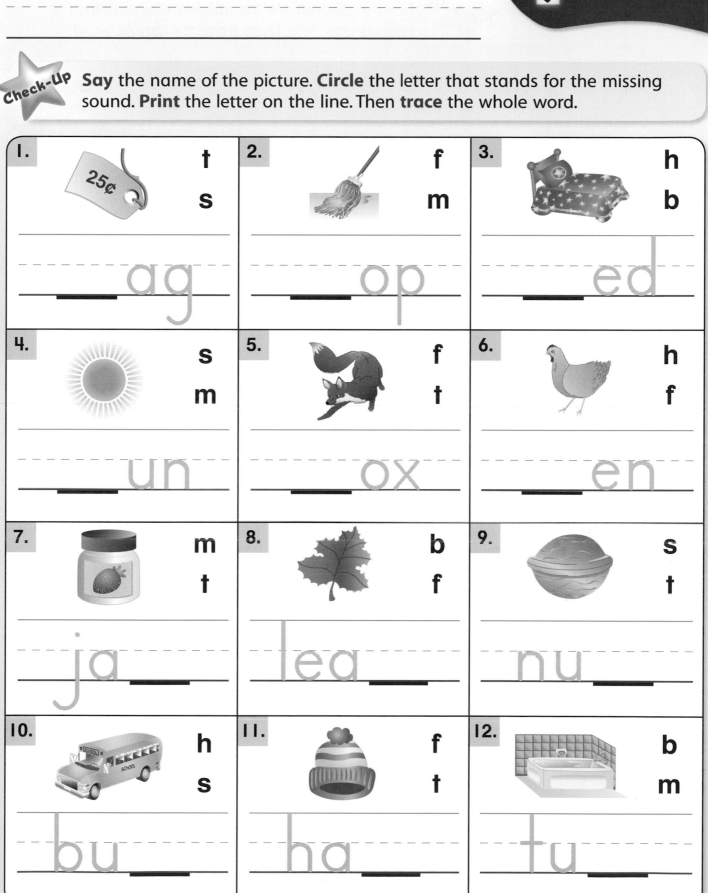

1. 25¢ t s ___ag	**2.** f m ___op	**3.** h b ___ed
4. s m ___un	**5.** f t ___ox	**6.** h f ___en
7. m t ja___	**8.** b f lea___	**9.** s t nu___
10. h s bu___	**11.** f t ha___	**12.** b m tu___

Check-Up

Say the name of the picture. **Find** the letter in the box that stands for the missing sound. **Print** the letter on the line. Then **trace** the whole word.

f	m	s	t	h	b

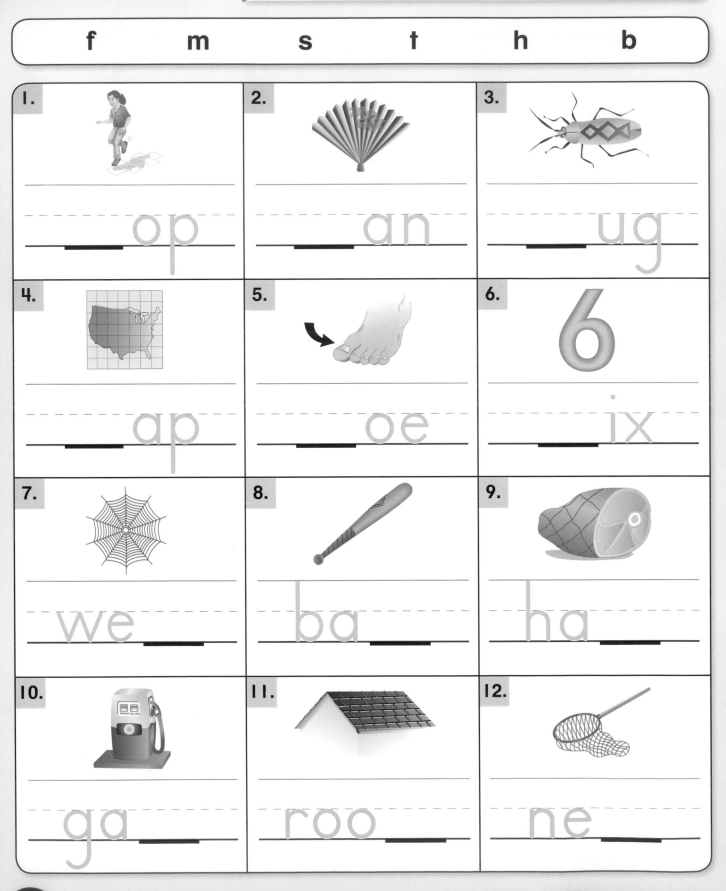

1. ___op

2. ___an

3. ___ug

4. ___ap

5. ___oe

6. ___ix

7. we___

8. ba___

9. ha___

10. ga___

11. roo___

12. ne___

Lesson 10 • Assessing Initial and Final
Consonants **f, m, s, t, h, b**

PHONICS ALIVE AT HOME
Review this Check-Up with your child.

Lunch starts with the sound of **l**.
Listen for the sound of **l** in the rhyme.

Lunch, lunch, lunch,
there's lots to eat.
Let's sit by the lake
and munch, munch, munch.

Say the name of the picture. **Print l** on the line if the picture name begins with the sound of **l**. Then **trace** the whole word.

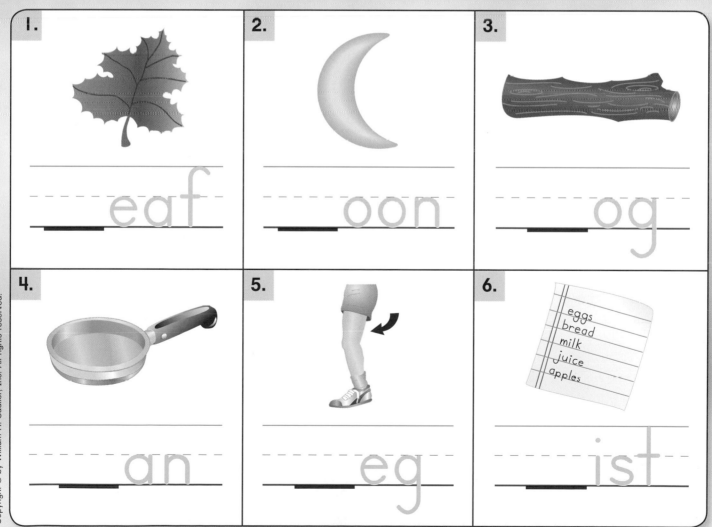

1. ___eaf

2. ___oon

3. ___og

4. ___an

5. ___eg

6. ___ist

eggs
bread
milk
juice
apples

Dd

Dance starts with the sound of **d**.
Listen for the sound of **d** in the rhyme.

Dance, dance, dance.
Get on your feet.
Dance, dance, dance.
Don't miss a beat.

Say the name of each picture. **Circle** the picture whose name begins with the sound of **d**. **Print d** on the line.

1.

2.

3.

4.

5.

6.

PHONICS
ALIVE AT HOME

Have a "treasure hunt" with your child and look for objects in your home that begin with the sound of **d**.

Cc

Caps starts with the sound of **c.**
Listen for the sound of **c** in the rhyme.

Casey comes in.
And so does her twin.
Our caps go up.
The Cubs win!

Say the name of the picture. **Print c** on the line if the picture name begins with the sound of **c.**

1.	2.	3.
4.	5.	6.
7.	8.	9.

Say the name of the picture. Circle the letter that stands for the ending sound. Print the letter on the line. Then trace the whole word.

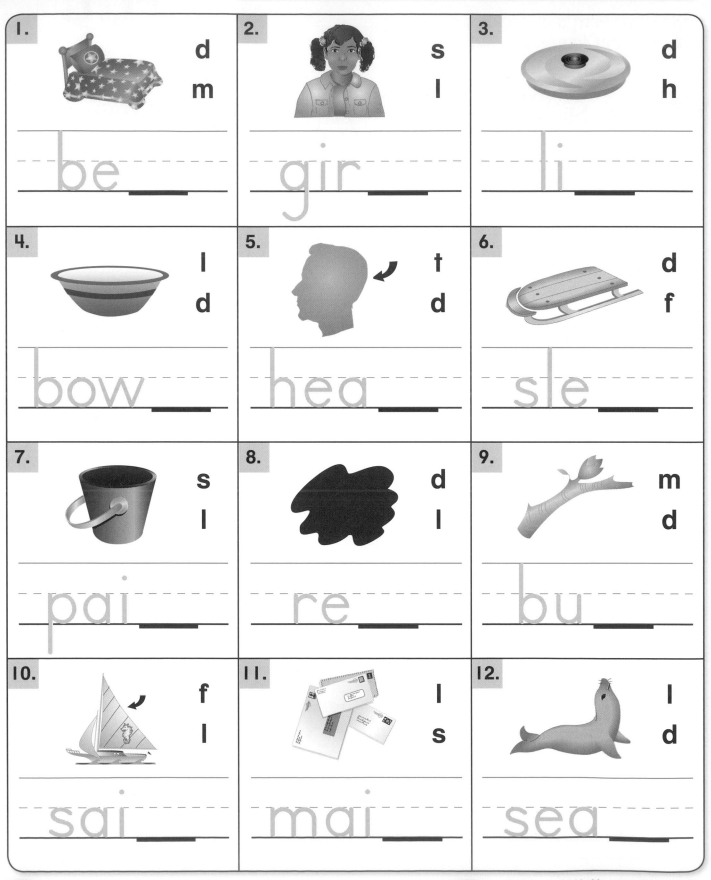

1.
d
m

be___

2.
s
l

gir___

3.
d
h

li___

4.
l
d

bow___

5.
t
d

hea___

6.
d
f

sle___

7.
s
l

pai___

8.
d
l

re___

9.
m
d

bu___

10.
f
l

sai___

11.
l
s

mai___

12.
l
d

sea___

Have your child hold up something red if he or she hears the sound of **d** at the end of these words: **had, nod, foil, peel, mad.**

Noise starts with the sound of **n. Listen** for the sound of **n** in the rhyme.

Make some noise
for number nine.
Nathan's next
to cross the line!

Say the name of the picture. **Print n** on the line if the picture name begins with the sound of **n.** Then **trace** the whole word.

1. ___ine

2. ___am

3. ___ut

4. ___ote

5. ___est

6. ___ail

Gift starts with the sound of **g**.
Listen for the sound of **g** in the rhyme.

Getting a gift
is good, it is true.
But giving a gift
is very good, too.

Say the name of each picture. **Circle** the picture whose name begins with the sound of **g**. **Print g** on the line.

1.

2.

3.

4.

5.

6.

PHONICS ALIVE AT HOME   Say "Give me a g!" Then have your child name a picture on the page that begins with the sound of **g**.

Waves starts with the sound of **w.**
Listen for the sound of **w** in the rhyme.

WILD WINDMILL

LINE UP HERE

Willy wiggles and giggles.
Willy watches and waves.
Willy's next!
Will he be brave?

Say the name of the picture. **Print w** on the line if the picture name
begins with the sound of **w.** Then **trace** the whole word.

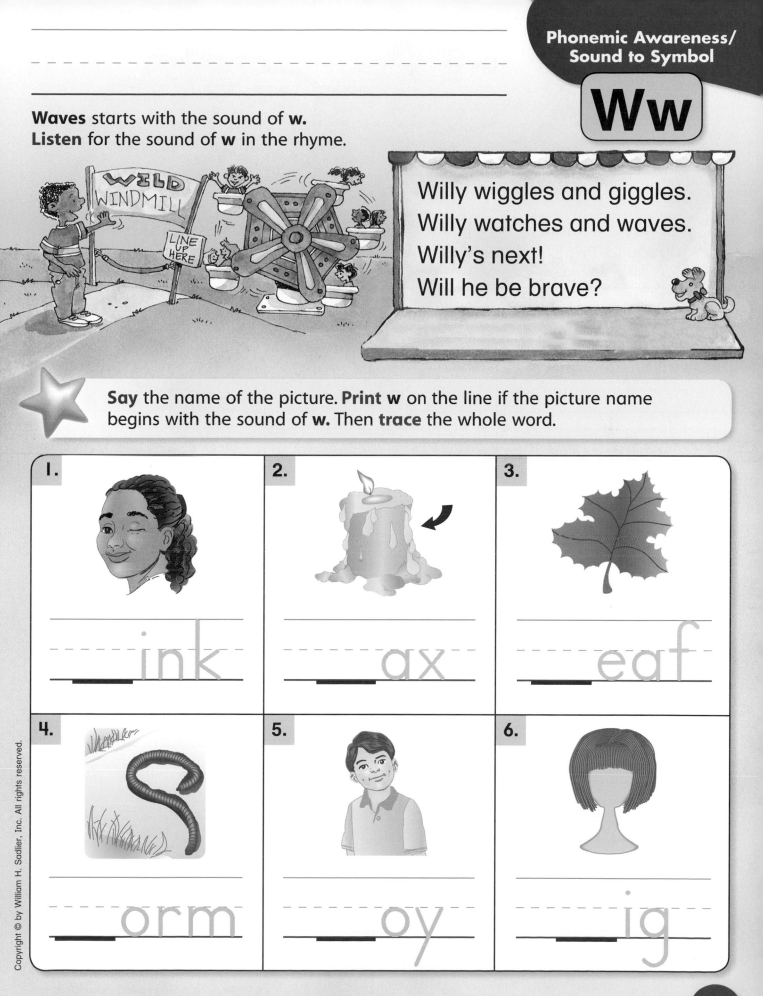

1. ___ink

2. ___ax

3. ___eaf

4. ___orm

5. ___oy

6. ___ig

Sound to Symbol

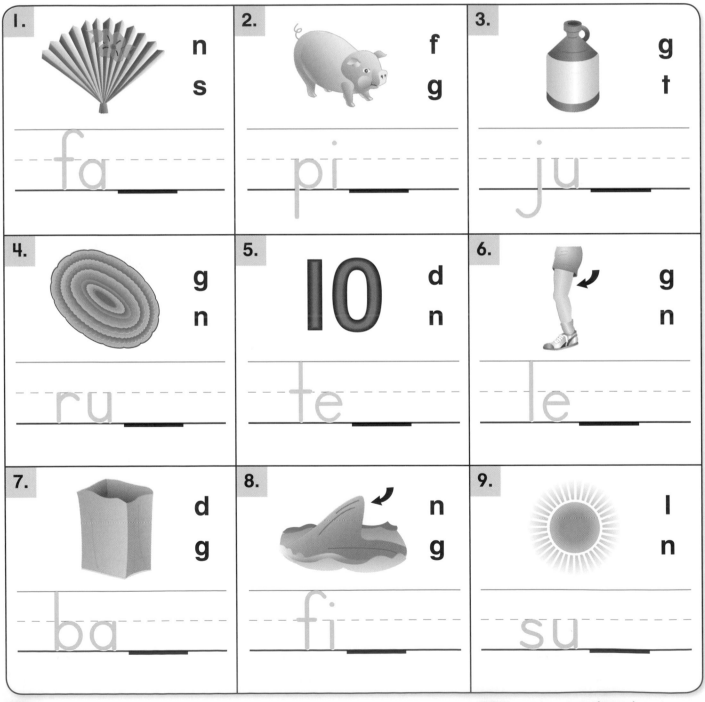

Say the name of the picture. **Circle** the letter that stands for the ending sound. **Print** the letter on the line. Then **trace** the whole word.

1. n s fa___	2. f g pi___	3. g t ju___
4. g n ru___	5. d n te___	6. g n le___
7. d g ba___	8. n g fi___	9. l n su___

Lesson 18 • Connecting Sound to Symbol:
Final /n/ n and /g/ g

PHONICS
ALIVE AT HOME

Take turns reading each word. Have your child name the letter that stands for the ending sound.

Assessment

Check-Up **Say** the name of the picture. **Circle** the letter that stands for the missing sound. **Print** the letter on the line. Then **trace** the whole word.

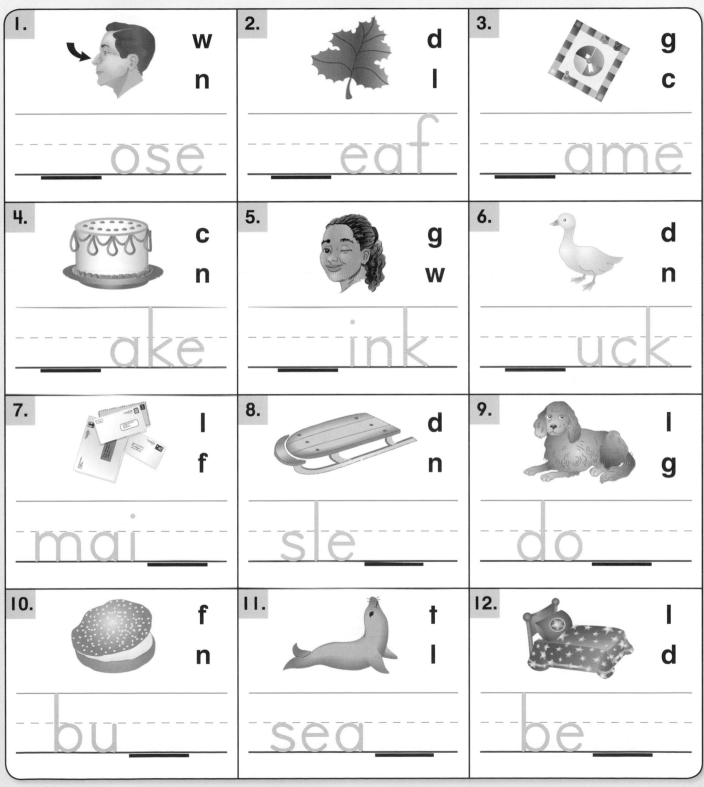

1. w n — ose
2. d l — eaf
3. g c — ame
4. c n — ake
5. g w — ink
6. d n — uck
7. l f — mai
8. d n — sle
9. l g — do
10. f n — bu
11. t l — sea
12. l d — be

Lesson 19 • Assessing Initial and Final Consonants l, d, c, n, g, w 25

Check-Up

Say the name of the picture. **Find** the letter in the box that stands for the missing sound. **Print** the letter on the line. Then **trace** the whole word.

l	d	c	n	g	w

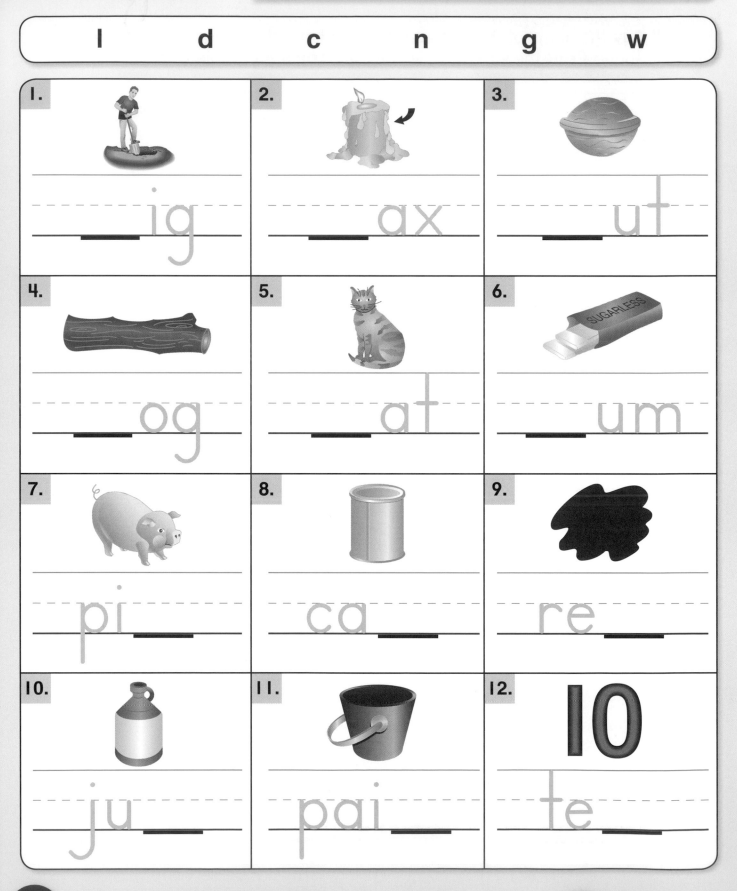

1. ___ ig

2. ___ ax

3. ___ ut

4. ___ og

5. ___ at

6. ___ um

7. pi ___

8. ca ___

9. re ___

10. ju ___

11. pai ___

12. te ___

PHONICS ALIVE AT HOME

Review this Check-Up with your child.

Ponies starts with the sound of **p.**
Listen for the sound of **p** in the rhyme.

Ponies and poodles
and parakeets, too.
They're having a pet parade
just for you.

Say the name of the picture. **Print p** on the line if the picture name
begins with the sound of **p.**

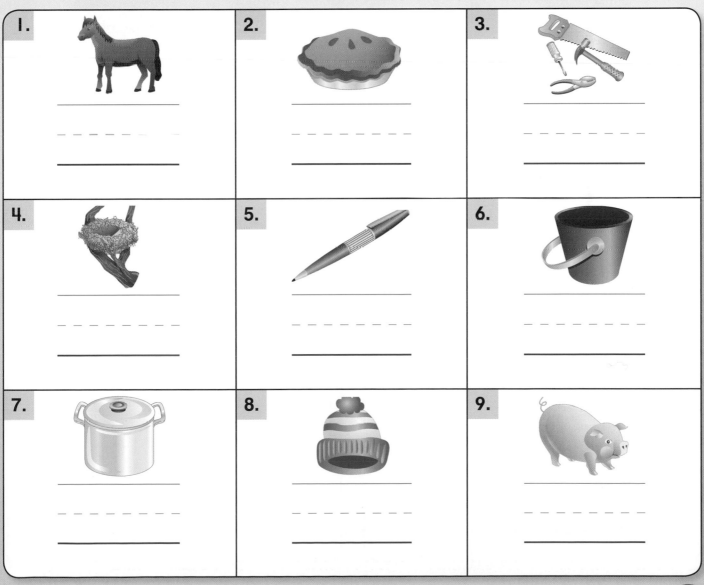

1.	2.	3.
4.	5.	6.
7.	8.	9.

Rr

Red starts with the sound of **r**.
Listen for the sound of **r** in the rhyme.

Red rover, red rover,
let Rosita come over.

Say the name of each picture. **Circle** the picture whose name begins with the sound of **r**. **Print r** on the line.

1.

2.

3.

4.

5.

6.

PHONICS
ALIVE AT HOME

Say the name of each picture.
Have your child repeat any name
that begins with the sound of **r**.

Kettle starts with the sound of k.
Listen for the sound of k in the rhyme.

Katie put the kettle on,
Katie put the kettle on,
Katie put the kettle on,
we'll all have tea.

Say the name of the picture. Print k on the line if the picture name begins with the sound of k. Then trace the whole word.

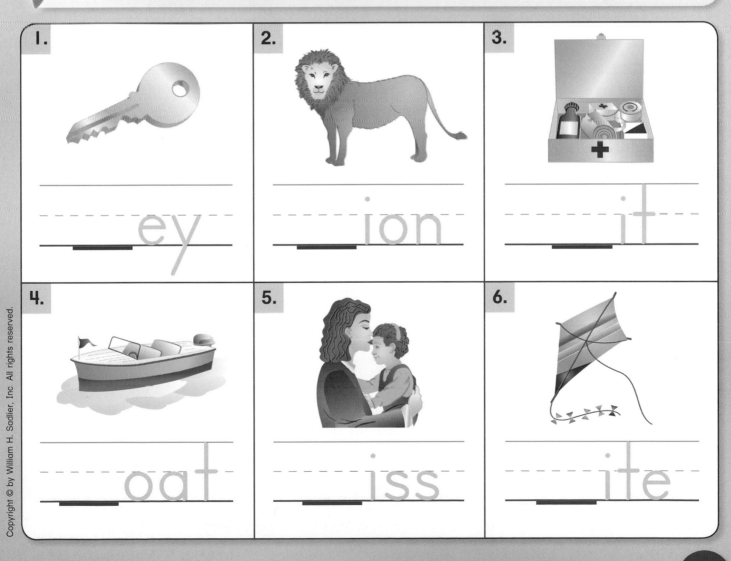

1. ___ ey

2. ___ ion

3. ___ it

4. ___ oat

5. ___ iss

6. ___ ite

Say the name of the picture. **Circle** the letter that stands for the ending sound. **Print** the letter on the line. Then **trace** the whole word.

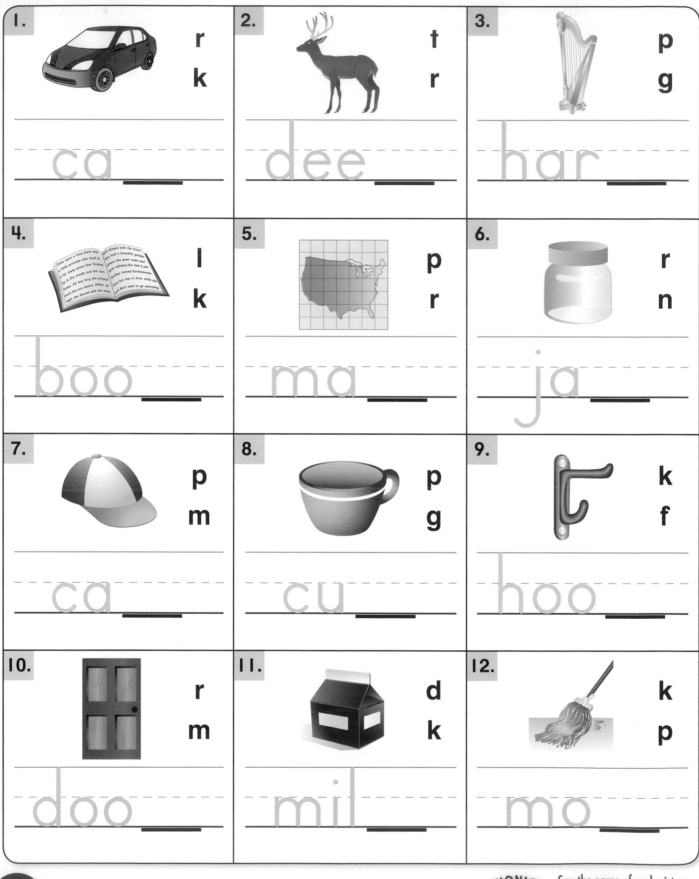

1. r
   k

   ca____

2. t
   r

   dee____

3. p
   g

   har____

4. l
   k

   boo____

5. p
   r

   ma____

6. r
   n

   ja____

7. p
   m

   ca____

8. p
   g

   cu____

9. k
   f

   hoo____

10. r
    m

    doo____

11. d
    k

    mil____

12. k
    p

    mo____

PHONICS ALIVE AT HOME Say the name of each picture. Have your child clap if its name ends with the sound of **p.**

Joy starts with the sound of **j**.
Listen for the sound of **j** in the rhyme.

Justin and Jasmin
jump for joy.
A brand new puppy
is better than a toy!

Say the name of each picture. **Circle** the picture whose name begins with the sound of **j**. **Print j** on the line.

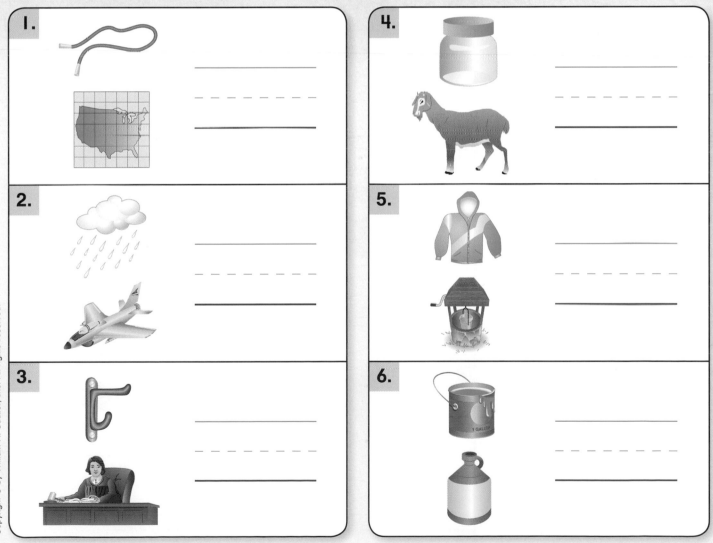

Qu qu

Quiet starts with the sound of **qu**.
Listen for the sound of **qu** in the rhyme.

"Shh! Quiet!" said the queen.
"Quick! Hide!" said the king.
Here comes Farmer Green!

Say the name of the picture. **Print qu** on the line if the picture name begins with the sound of **qu**.

1.	2.	3.
4.	5.	6.
7.	8.	9.

PHONICS
ALIVE AT HOME

Point to a picture on the page. If the picture starts with the sound of **qu**, have your child say, "Quiet!"

Vase starts with the sound of **v.**
Listen for the sound of **v** in the rhyme.

A big vase of violets
and velvet hearts, too,
are the Valentine gifts
I'd like to give to you.

Say the name of the picture. **Print v** on the line if the picture name
begins with the sound of **v.** Then **trace** the whole word.

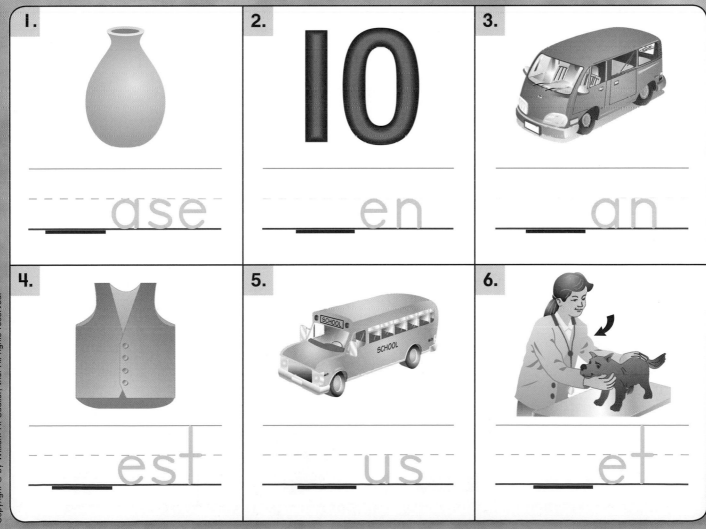

1. _ase

2. _en

3. _an

4. _est

5. _us

6. _et

Say the name of each picture. **Circle** the picture if its name ends with the sound of **v. Print v** on the line.

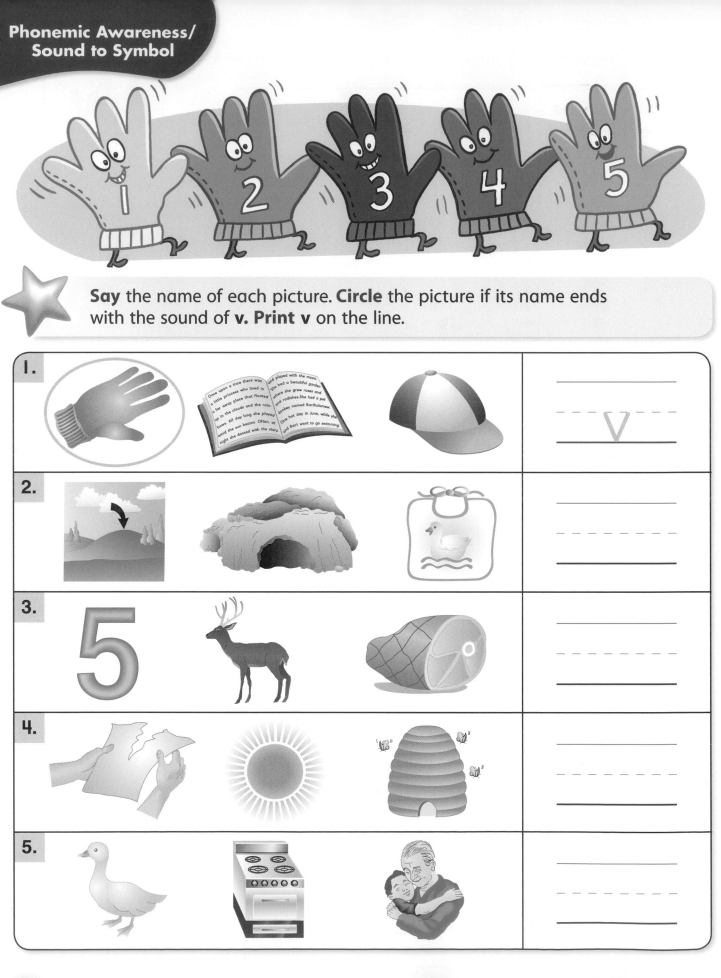

1.   V

2.

3.

4.

5.

Lesson 27 • Phonemic Awareness
Connecting Sound to Symbol:
Final /v/ v

PHONICS
ALIVE AT HOME

Say the name of each picture. Have your child make a "v" with his or her index and middle fingers when you say a word that ends with the sound of **v.**

Yy
Zz

Year starts with the sound of **y**. **Zero** starts with the sound of **z**.
Listen for the sounds of **y** and **z** in the rhyme.

Count down to zero.
Yell out a loud cheer.
The old year is out.
The new year is here.

Hello, New Year

Say the name of the picture. **Print y** on the line if the picture name begins with the sound of **y**. **Print z** on the line if the picture name begins with the sound of **z**.

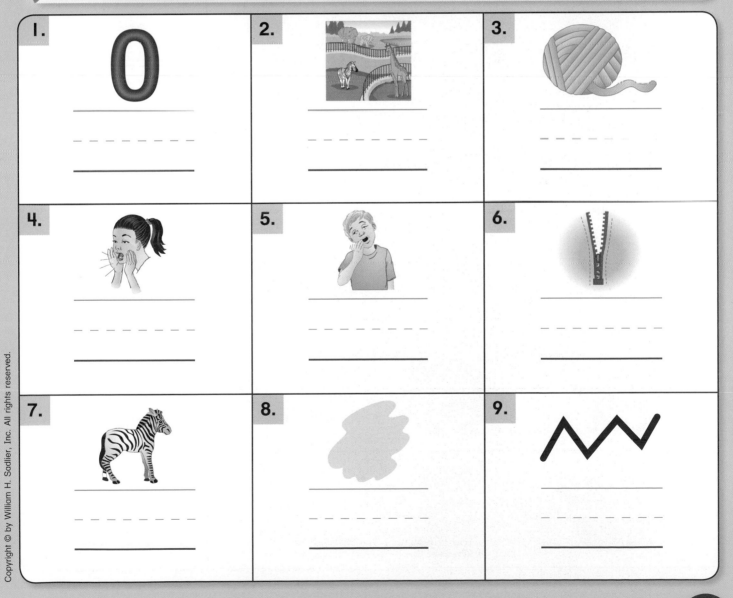

I.	2.	3.
4.	5.	6.
7.	8.	9.

Xx

Box ends with the sound of **x**.
Listen for the sound of **x** in the rhyme.

I can't wait to see,
the toys for me—
a box of clay, a sax to play,
I love a fun piñata day!

Say the name of each picture. **Circle** the picture if its name ends with the sound of **x. Print x** on the line.

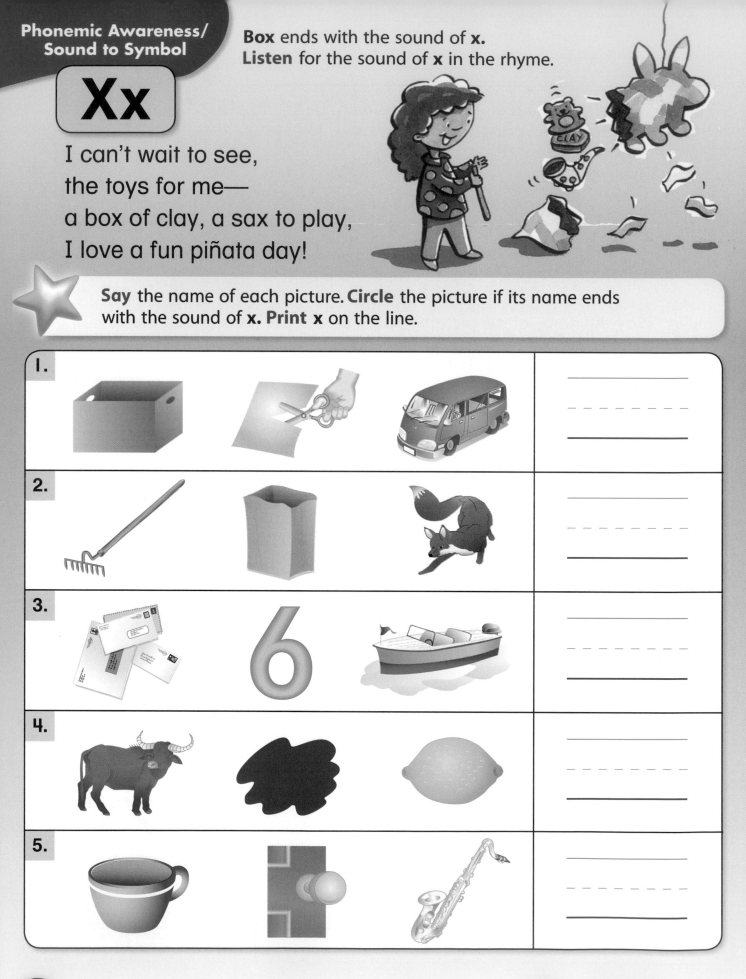

1.

2.

3.

4.

5.

Lesson 29 • Phonemic Awareness
Connecting Sound to Symbol: Final /ks/ x

PHONICS ALIVE AT HOME

Have your child make up a sentence using the name of each picture he or she circled.

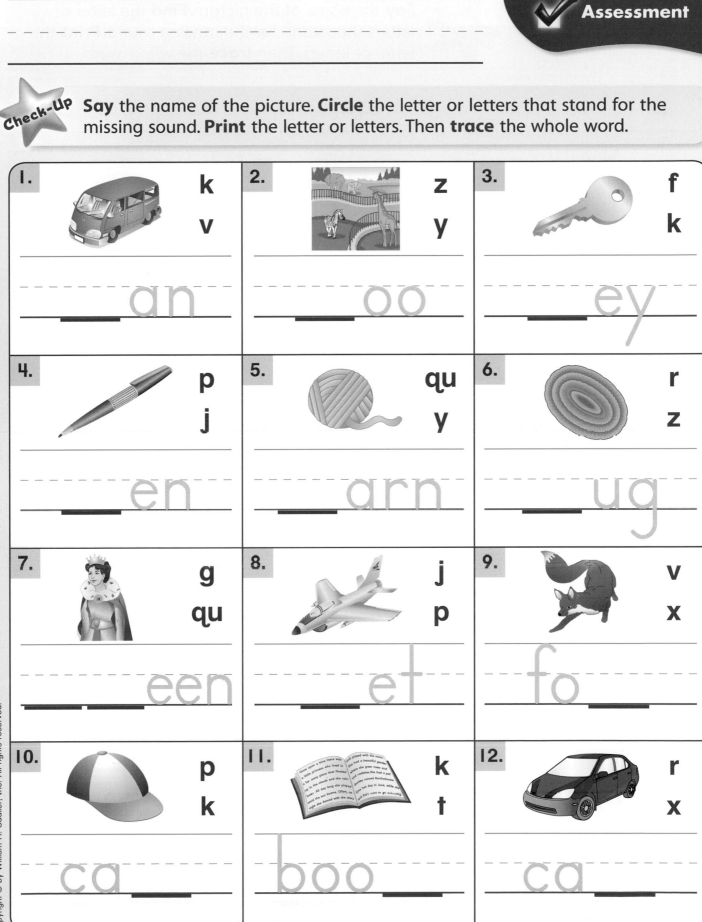

Check-Up **Say** the name of the picture. **Circle** the letter or letters that stand for the missing sound. **Print** the letter or letters. Then **trace** the whole word.

1.	k v	_an
2.	z y	_oo
3.	f k	_ey
4.	p j	_en
5.	qu y	_arn
6.	r z	_ug
7.	g qu	_een
8.	j p	_et
9.	v x	fo_
10.	p k	ca_
11.	k t	boo_
12.	r x	ca_

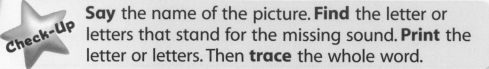

Check-Up

Say the name of the picture. **Find** the letter or letters that stand for the missing sound. **Print** the letter or letters. Then **trace** the whole word.

| p | r | k | j | qu | v | x | y | z |

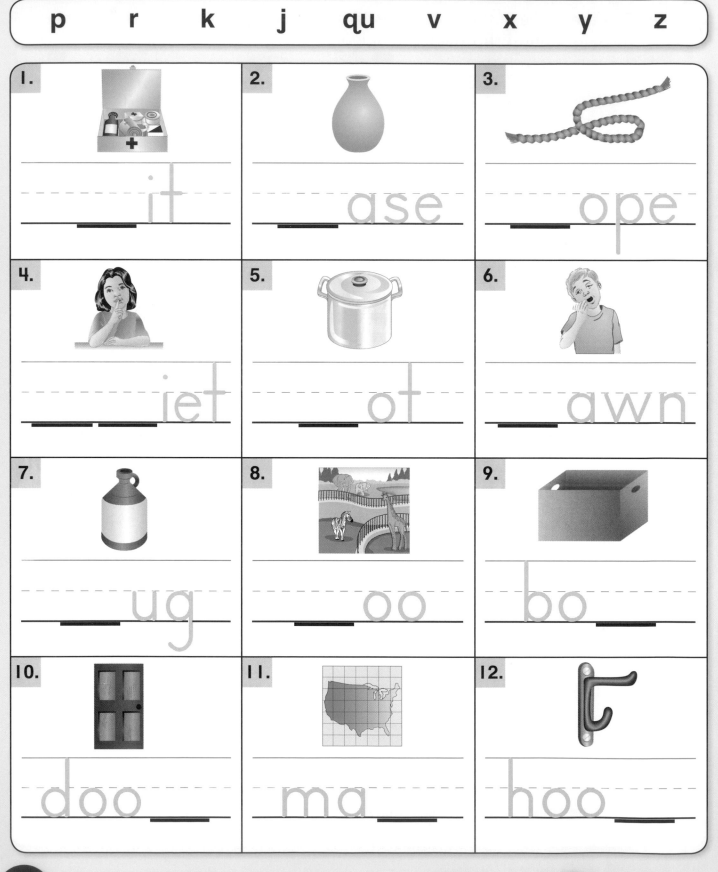

1. ___it

2. ___ase

3. ___ope

4. ___iet

5. ___ot

6. ___awn

7. ___ug

8. ___oo

9. ___bo___

10. doo___

11. ma___

12. hoo___

PHONICS
ALIVE AT HOME

Review this Check-Up
with your child.

ff
ss
tt

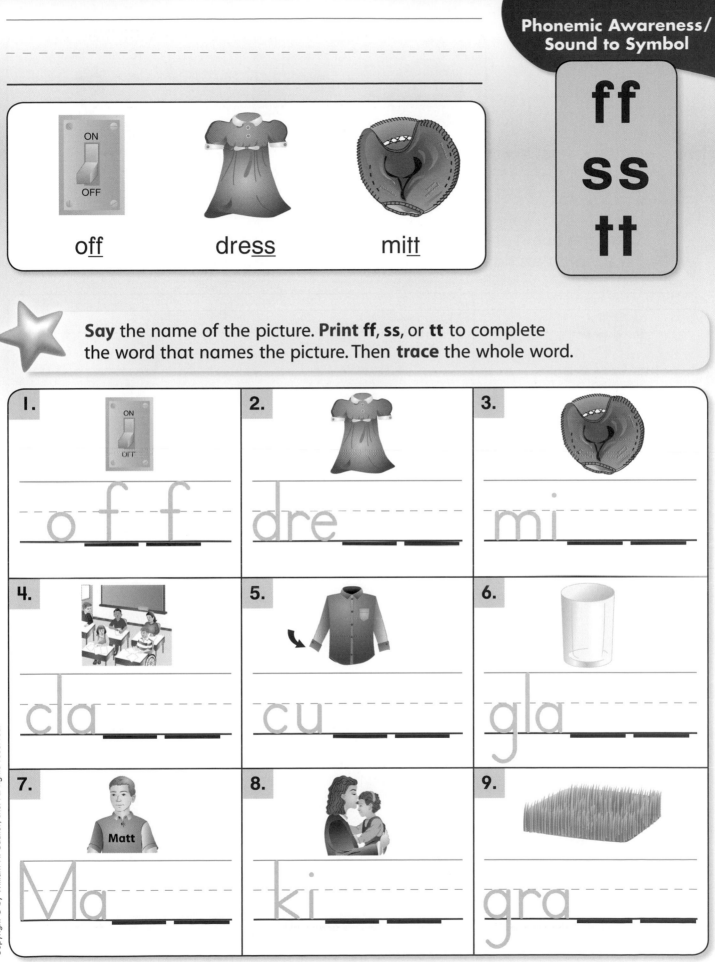

off   dress   mitt

Say the name of the picture. **Print ff, ss,** or **tt** to complete
the word that names the picture. Then **trace** the whole word.

1. o f f

2. dre ___

3. mi ___

4. cla ___

5. cu ___

6. gla ___

7. Matt Ma ___

8. ki ___

9. gra ___

ll dd gg zz

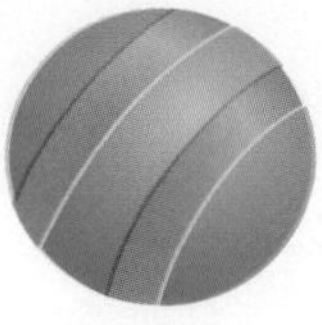

ba<u>ll</u>   a<u>dd</u> 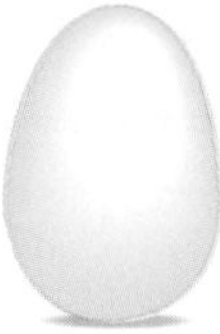   e<u>gg</u> 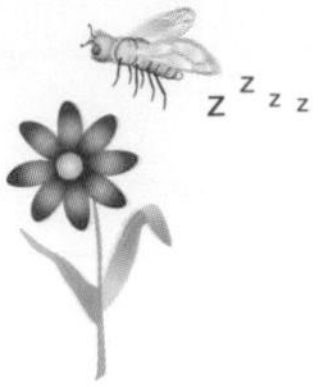   bu<u>zz</u>

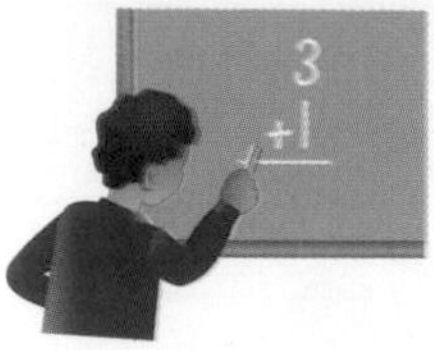

Say the name of the picture. **Print ll, dd, gg,** or **zz** to complete the word that names the picture. Then **trace** the whole word.

1.

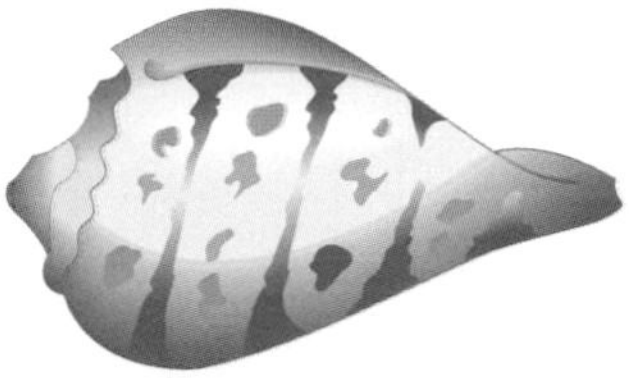

she___

2.

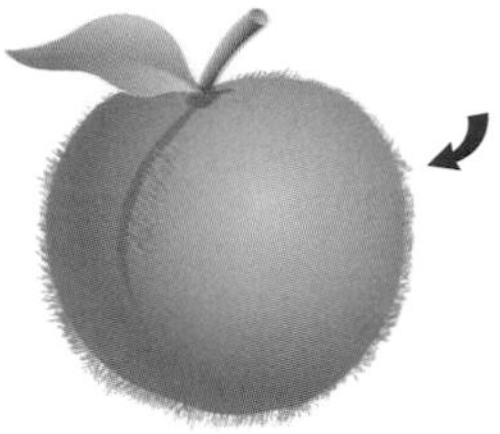

fu___

3.

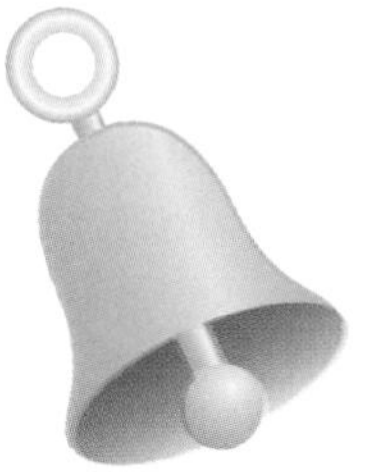

be___

4.

e___

5.

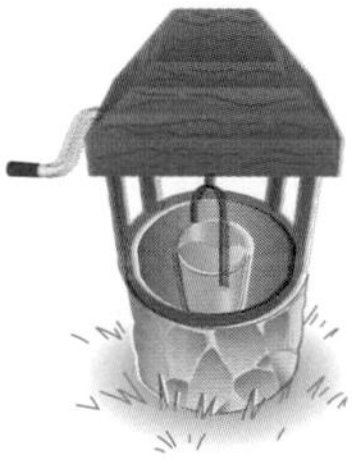

we___

6.

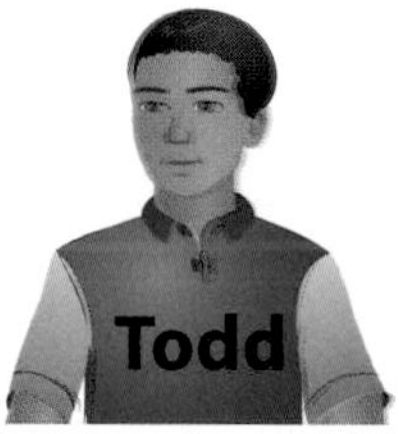

Todd

To___

7.

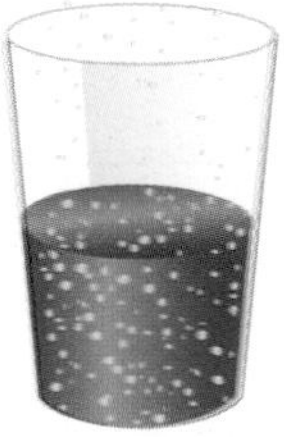

fi___

8.

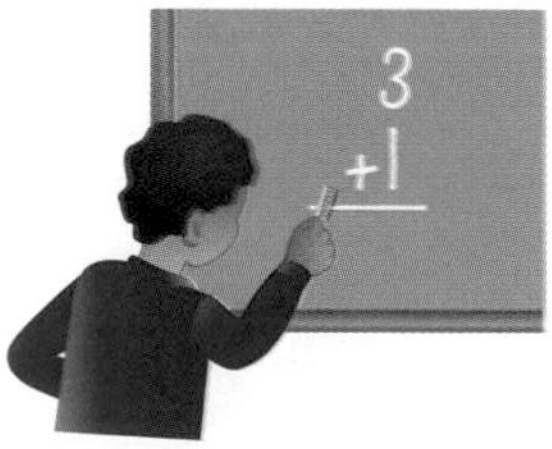

a___

9.

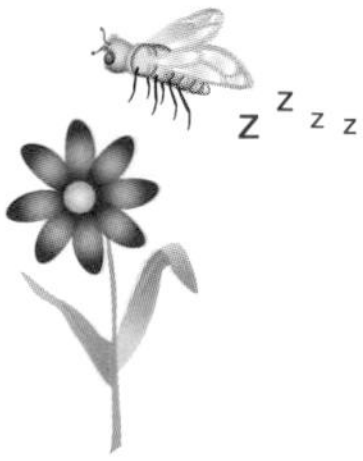

bu___

Summer has the sound of **m** in the middle. **Listen** for the middle consonant sounds in the rhyme.

Bobbing for apples,
a three-legged run,
and riding on ponies,
make summer great fun!

Say the name of the picture. **Circle** the letter that stands for the middle consonant sound.

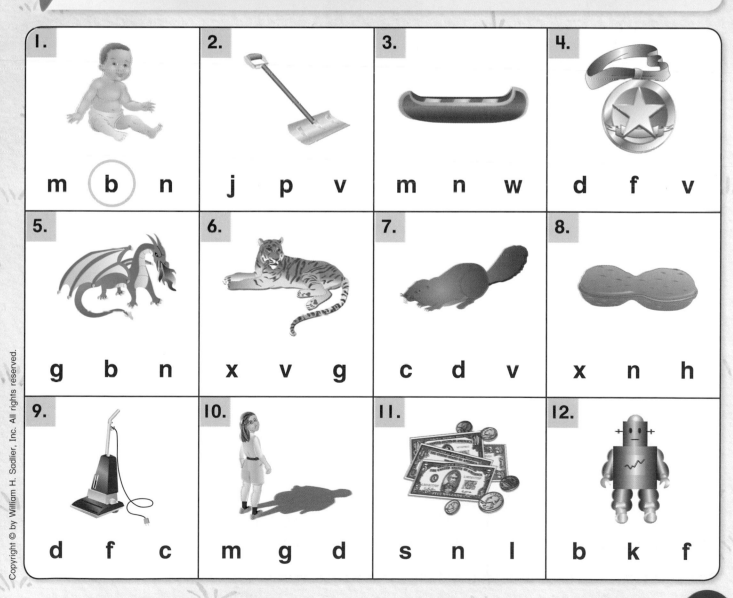

I. m (b) n	**2.** j p v	**3.** m n w	**4.** d f v
5. g b n	**6.** x v g	**7.** c d v	**8.** x n h
9. d f c	**10.** m g d	**II.** s n l	**12.** b k f

Say the name of the picture. **Print** the letter that stands for the middle consonant sound. Then **trace** the whole word.

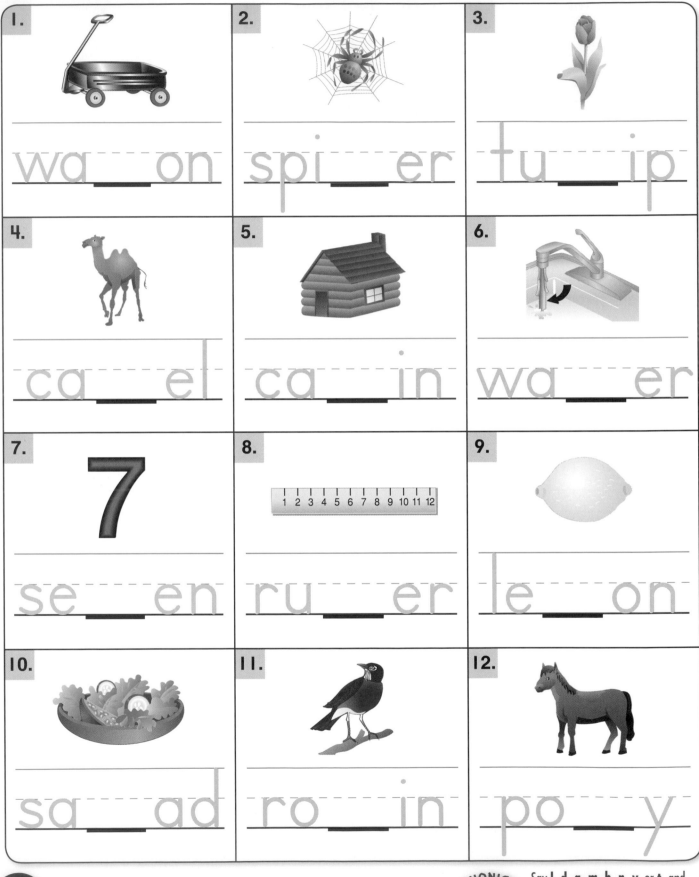

1. wa___on

2. spi___er

3. tu___ip

4. ca___el

5. ca___in

6. wa___er

7. se___en

8. ru___er

9. le___on

10. sa___ad

11. ro___in

12. po___y

PHONICS ALIVE AT HOME

Say **l, d, g, m, b, n, v,** or **t,** and have your child point to a picture with that letter in the middle of its name.

Use one of the words in the box to complete each sentence. Practice **reading** the sentences aloud.

by	funny	Let	ride	Stop	walk

1. The 🐰🐰 run _____ **by** _____ me.

2. The 🐻🐻 _____ by me.

3. The 🤡🤡 _____ by me.

4. I like the _____ 🤸🤡.

5. _____! Let me walk with you.

6. _____ me be funny, too!

Review

Circle the word in the box that completes each sentence. **Print** the word on the line. **Read** the sentences.

1. I walk _____ by _____ the ride.

   by
   that

2. You _____ with me.

   walk
   funny

3. I stop for a _____ .

   ride
   you

4. You _____ for a ride, too.

   me
   stop

5. I _____ you ride with me.

   is
   let

Check-Up

Color a 😊 for each word you wrote.

😊 stop   😊 let   😊 by   😊 me   😊 walk

😊 that   😊 is   😊 ride   😊 you   😊 funny

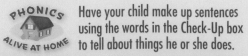

PHONICS ALIVE AT HOME

Have your child make up sentences using the words in the Check-Up box to tell about things he or she does.

READ Look at the pictures. **Read** the page. **Talk** about what you see.

Learn About Celebrations

We can celebrate in many ways. We can have a parade. We can also make food, sing songs, and wear costumes. The people in the pictures are celebrating the new year. They made a big dragon.

How do you celebrate special times?

Phonics and Writing

The Big Party

The animal friends are having a big party. See who is invited! **Print** a consonant to complete each animal name. **Look** at the letters in the box if you need help.

l	d	p	g

g	t	b	x

1. ___ ig

2. ___ oat

3. ___ ion

4. ___ uck

5. ___ ca ___

6. ___ do ___

7. ___ fo ___

8. ___ cu ___

Lesson 35 • Writing Initial and Final
Consonants in Context

PHONICS
ALIVE AT HOME

Have your child read the animal names he or she wrote.
Ask your child to name other things in the picture and name
the letters that stand for the beginning or ending sound.

 **Assessment**

⭐ **Check-Up** **Say** the name of the picture. **Print** the letter or letters that stand for the missing sound on the line. Then **trace** the whole word.

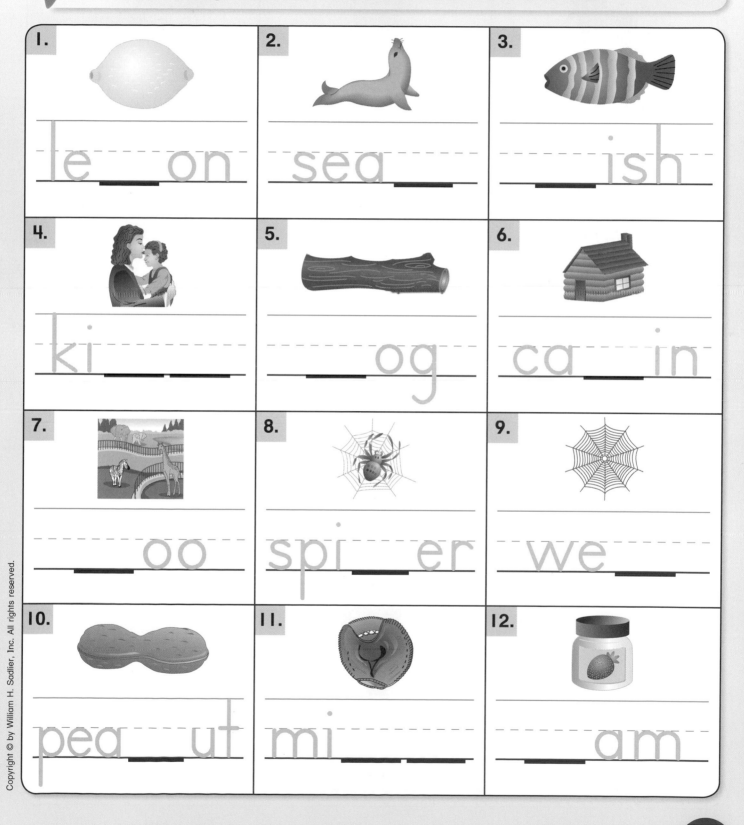

1. le___on
2. sea___
3. ___ish
4. ki___
5. ___og
6. ca___in
7. ___oo
8. spi___er
9. we___
10. pea___ut
11. mi___
12. ___am

✓ **Assessment**

Check-Up

Say the name of the picture. **Print** the letter or letters that stand for the missing sound on the line. Then **trace** the whole word.

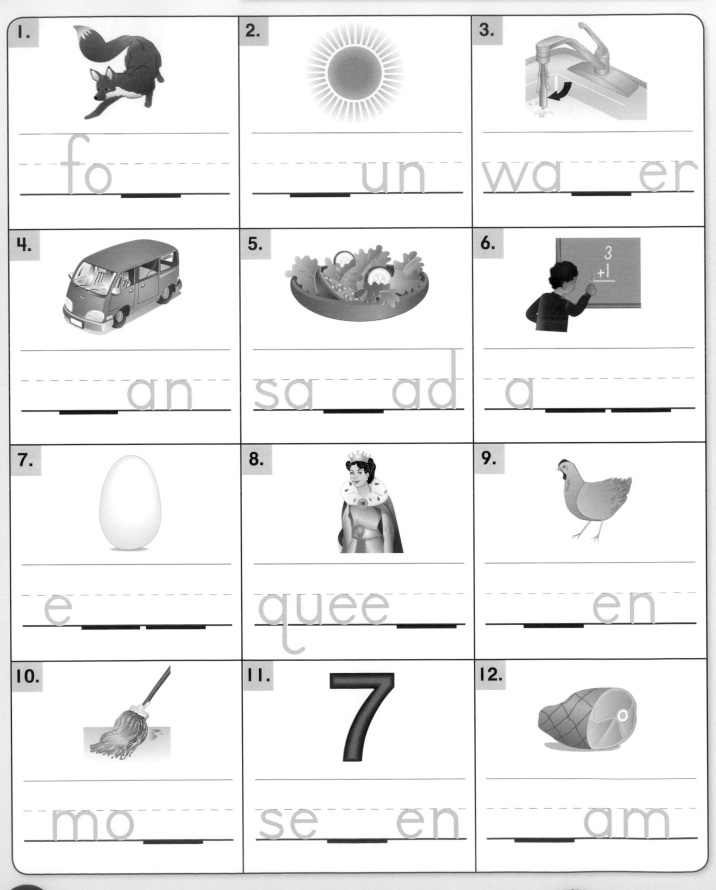

1. fo___

2. ___un

3. wa___er

4. ___an

5. sa___ad

6. a___

7. e___

8. quee___

9. ___en

10. mo___

11. se___en

12. ___am

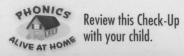

PHONICS ALIVE AT HOME

Review this Check-Up with your child.

Name _____

I LOVE PARADES

Fold

Reading at Home: Read the book together. Listen for beginning and ending consonant sounds. Then ask your child to tell the story in order.

1

3

with funny clowns,

Fold

and me!
Draw a picture to show
what you do in the parade.

8

razzle-dazzle
floats that ride by,

6

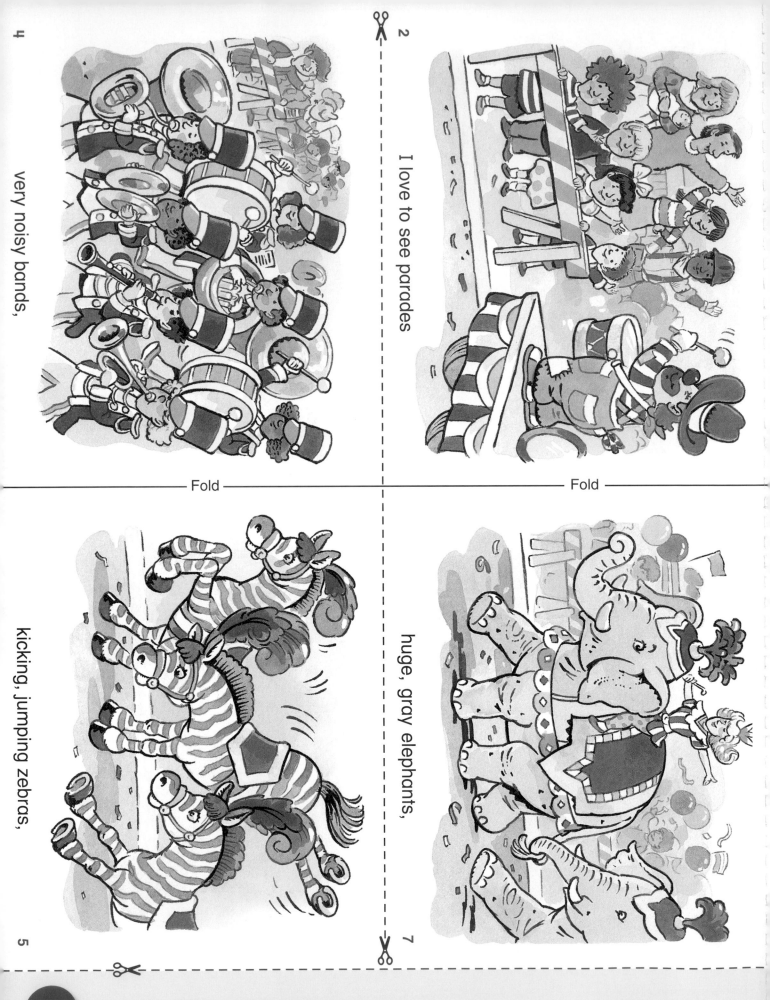

4

very noisy bands,

2

I love to see parades

— Fold —

— Fold —

kicking, jumping zebras,

5

huge, gray elephants,

7

BUGS

I like bugs.
Black bugs,
Green bugs,
Bad bugs,
Mean bugs,
Any kind of bug,

A bug in a rug,
A bug in the grass,
A bug on the sidewalk,
A bug in a glass—
I like bugs.

Round bugs,
Shiny bugs,
Fat bugs,
Buggy bugs,
Big bugs,
Ladybugs,
I like bugs.

Margaret Wise Brown

Oral Language How are these bugs different?
How do different kinds of bugs move?

PHONICS ALIVE AT HOME

Name _____

Dear Family,

In this unit, your child will learn the sounds of the short vowels. She or he will also be thinking and reading about bugs. As your child progresses through this unit, you can make phonics come alive at home with these activities.

- Look at the pictures below. Say each letter and picture name with your child. Listen to the vowel sound.

Apreciada Familia:

En esta unidad los niños aprenderán los sonidos cortos de las vocales. También pensarán y leerán sobre insectos. A medida que se avanza en la unidad, ustedes pueden revivir los fonemas en casa con estas actividades.

- Miren los grabados. Pronuncien juntos cada letra y el nombre del objeto. Escuchen el sonido de la vocal.

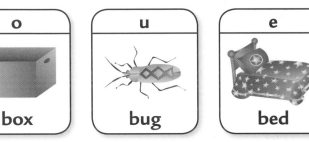

a	i	o	u	e
cat	six	box	bug	bed

- Read the poem "Bugs" on the reverse side of this page as your child follows along. Talk about the bugs you see.

- Help your child find some of the short vowel words in the poem, such as **bugs, black, bad, rug, on, glass, fat,** and **big.**

- Say these words one at a time: **bug, fat,** and **big.** Ask your child to say the three sounds heard in each word. (**b-u-g, f-a-t, b-i-g**)

- Lea el poema "Bugs" en la página 51 mientras su hijo lo repite. Hablen acerca de los insectos que ven.

- Ayude a su hijo a encontrar algunas vocales de sonido corto en las palabras del poema, como: **bugs, black, bad, rug, on, glass, fat** y **big.**

- Pronuncie estas palabras una por una: **bug, fat** y **big.** Pida a su hijo que diga los tres sonidos que se oyen en cada palabra. (**b-u-g, f-a-t, b-i-g**)

PROJECT   PROYECTO

Together with your child, draw a "never seen before" bug. Will it have spots? What kind of wings will it have? Give your new bug a name. Next to your picture, print five or six words that describe it.

Dibujen un "insecto nunca visto". ¿Tendrá manchas? ¿Qué tipo de alas tendrá? Pónganle un nombre al nuevo insecto. Escriban cinco o seis palabras para describirlo.

 Visit us at **www.sadlierphonicsonline.com**

Listen as the page is read aloud. **Talk** about the short **a** words you hear, such as **can** and **pack**. **Act out** the story.

I Can

I **can pack** a **bag**.
An ant can't.

I **can tag** a **pal**.
An ant can't.

I **can clap** my **hands**.
An ant can't.

I **can** hide in the **grass**.
And an ant can, too!

Oral Language What are some things an ant can do that you can't?

Sound to Symbol

Cat has the short **a** sound. **Say** the name of the picture. **Print a** on the line under each picture that has the short **a** sound in its name.

c<u>a</u>t	**1.** _____ a _____	**2.** _____ _____	**3.** _____ _____
4. _____ _____	**5.** _____ _____	**6.** _____ _____	**7.** _____ _____
8. _____ _____	**9.** _____ _____	**10.** _____ _____	**11.** _____ _____
12. _____ _____	**13.** _____ _____	**14.** _____ _____	**15.** _____ _____

PHONICS ALIVE AT HOME — Say the name of the picture. Ask your child to tap you if the name has the short **a** sound.

Trace the line as you blend the sounds together to say the word.
Circle the picture named.

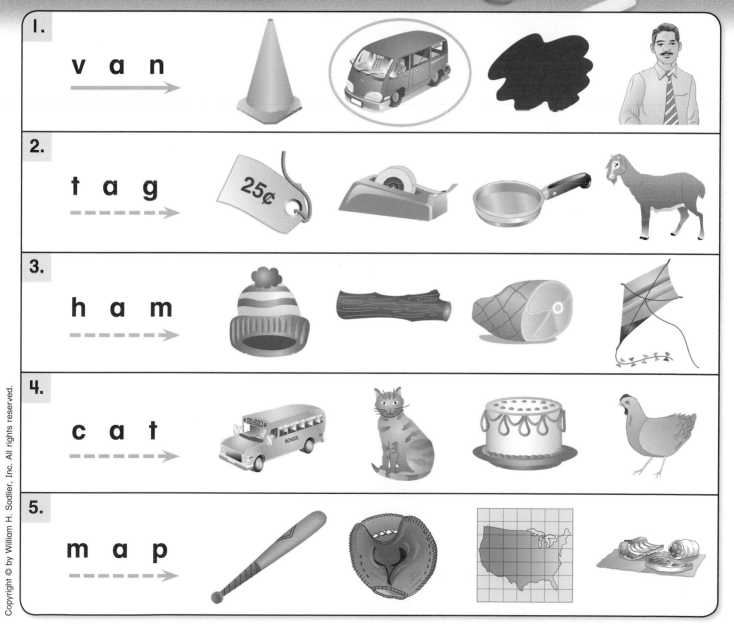

1. v a n →

2. t a g →

3. h a m →

4. c a t →

5. m a p →

Blending Phonemes

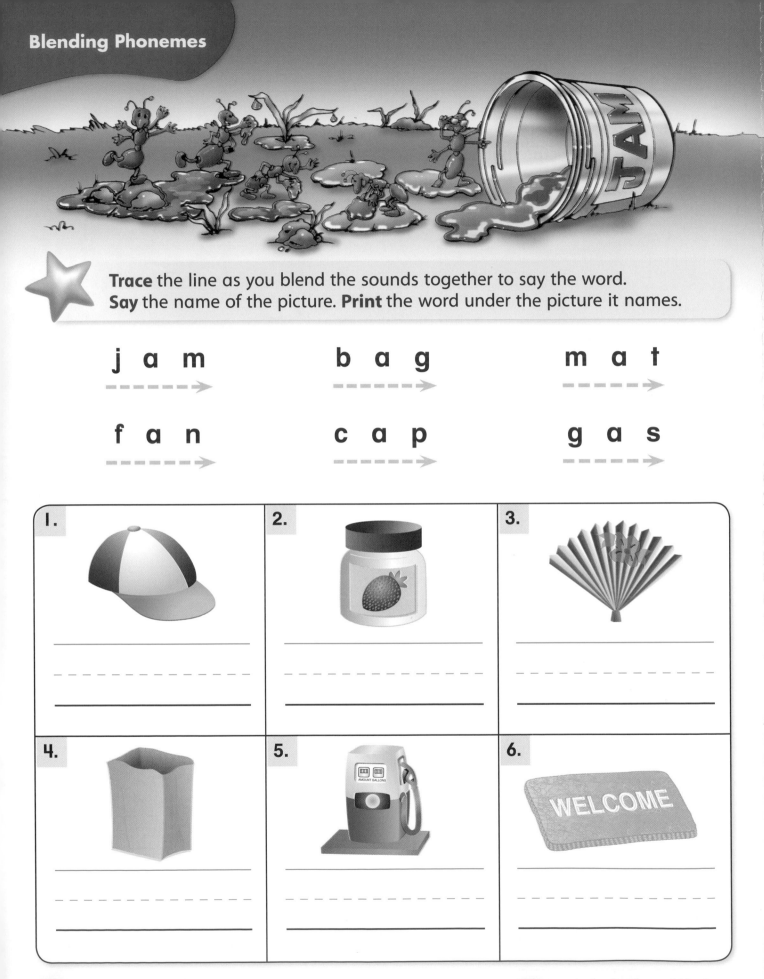

Trace the line as you blend the sounds together to say the word.
Say the name of the picture. **Print** the word under the picture it names.

j a m

b a g

m a t

f a n

c a p

g a s

1.

2.

3.

4.

5.

6.

PHONICS
ALIVE AT HOME

Clap hands with your child as he or she says the three sounds heard in each word on this page: **f-a-n.**

⭐ **Say** the name of each picture. In each row, **circle** two pictures that have rhyming names. Make a new rhyming word. **Print** it on the line.

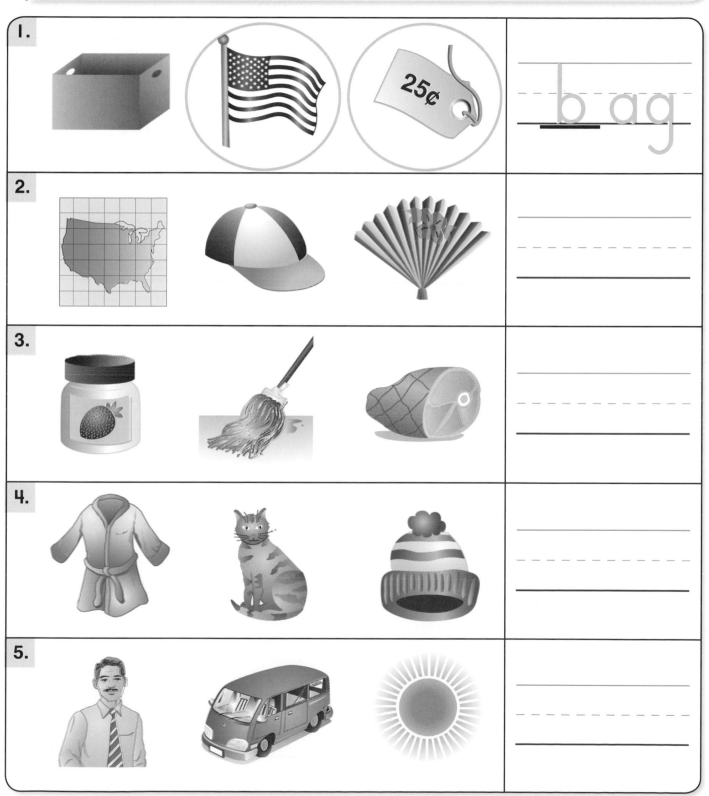

Trace the line as you blend the sounds together to say the word. **Print** the word on the line. **Circle** the picture it names.

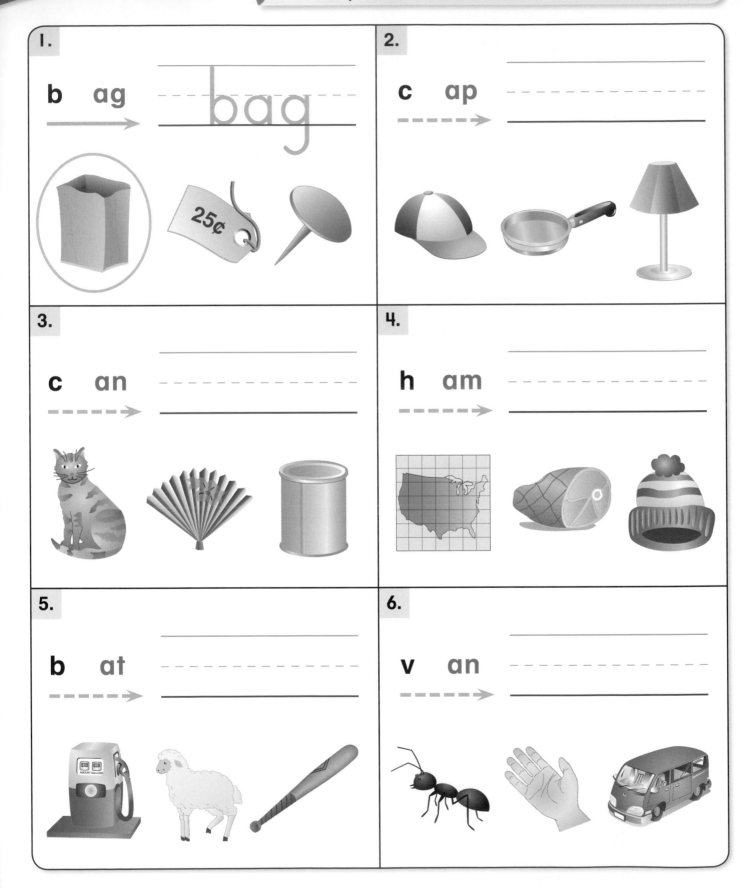

1. b ag

bag

2. c ap

3. c an

4. h am

5. b at

6. v an

PHONICS ALIVE AT HOME   Have your child select one word on the page and together build a list of rhyming words.

Trace the line as you blend the sounds together to say the word.
Say the name of the picture. Print the word under the picture it names.

c at

m ap

f an

b ag

b at

v an

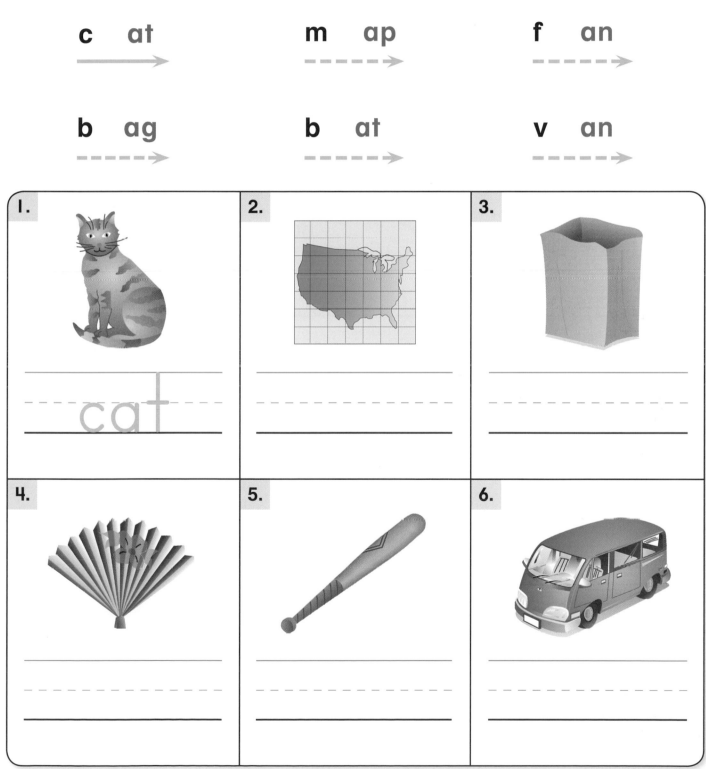

1.

cat

2.

3.

4.

5.

6.

Say the name of the picture. **Circle** its name and **print** it on the line.

1. fat tan (fan)	2. ham hat jam	3. and ant ax
fan		

4. bag bad grab	5. band pat bat	6. pal pan plan

7. rap map pad	8. camp cat sat	9. land damp hand

Make up and **print** a sentence with a short **a** word.

PHONICS ALIVE AT HOME — Fold a sheet of paper like an accordion to make a fan. Help your child write a short **a** word on each pleat.

Read

Name _____

PAT

Then Pat can nap. Pat LIKES to nap!

8

Pat just got up. What can Pat do today?

1

Then Pat can tap. Pat likes to tap.

6

Then Pat can do her job. Pat likes her job.

3

DIRECTIONS: Cut and fold the book. Read the story. If you come to a word you don't know, sound it out by looking at each letter. Tell the different things Pat does.

Lesson 43 • Short Vowel **a** Reader
Comprehension:
Recalling Details

61

First Pat can jog. Pat likes
2 to jog.

After all of that, Pat can
stop.   7

Then Pat can jump. Pat
4 likes to jump.

Then Pat can bat. Pat likes
to bat.   5

Lesson 43 • Short Vowel a Reader
Comprehension: Recalling Details

Look at the picture. **Circle** the word that completes the sentence.
Print it on the line.

1.	Dan got his _____ .	fat bat bad
2.	He _____ up the hill.	rap pan ran
3.	His _____ fell off.	cap cat can
4.	Dan _____ on the log.	sat rat mat
5.	He felt a bug on his _____ .	ham sand hand
6.	It was just a little _____ .	ax ant tan

Read the poem. Use short **a** words to complete the sentences.

My Ant Farm

My pet ants like to
snack on jam.
I give them names
like Ann, Pam, and Sam.

I hand them lots of
scraps and grass.
Then I watch them
in the glass.

1. Jam is a _____ for the ants.

2. The ants are Ann, Pam, and _____ .

3. You can watch them in the _____ .

Lesson 44 • Short Vowel **a** in Context
Comprehension: Recalling Details

PHONICS ALIVE AT HOME
Read the poem to your child. Talk about other things Ann, Pam, and Sam might do.

Read the story. **Print** three short **a** words from the story and three more short **a** words that you know. Then **read** all the words you wrote.

Sam and Jan

A bat and a cat!
The bat is for Sam.
The cat is for Jan.

A fan and a pan!
The fan is for Sam.
The pan is for Jan.

A hat and a mat!
The hat is for Sam.
The mat is for Jan.

The cab is for Sam and Jan!

For Sale

Sidewalk Sale

CAB

Story Words

1. _____

2. _____

3. _____

My Words

1. _____

2. _____

3. _____

Ham with Jam

Ann the Ant and Pat the Cat are having a picnic. **Write** about what you see. Use some short **a** words. **Look** at the words in the box if you need help.

Ann	Pat	ant	cat	bag
ham	jam	can	cap	nap

PHONICS ALIVE AT HOME Have your child read the short **a** words in the box. Have him or her use the words in sentences.

Print the name of each picture in the puzzle. Some words will go across. Some words will go down. Print only one letter in each box.

ACROSS ➡

1. 3. 5. 25¢

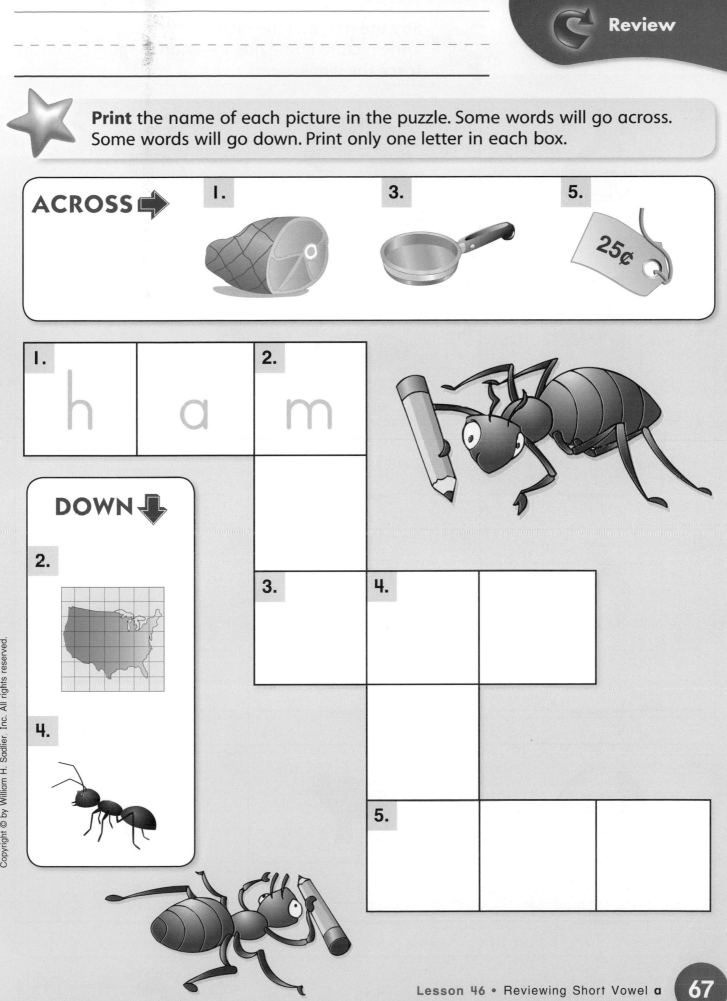

1. | h | a | m |

DOWN ⬇

2.

4.

3. 4.

5.

Check-Up

Say the name of the picture. **Print a** on the line if the picture name has the short **a** sound. Then **trace** the whole word.

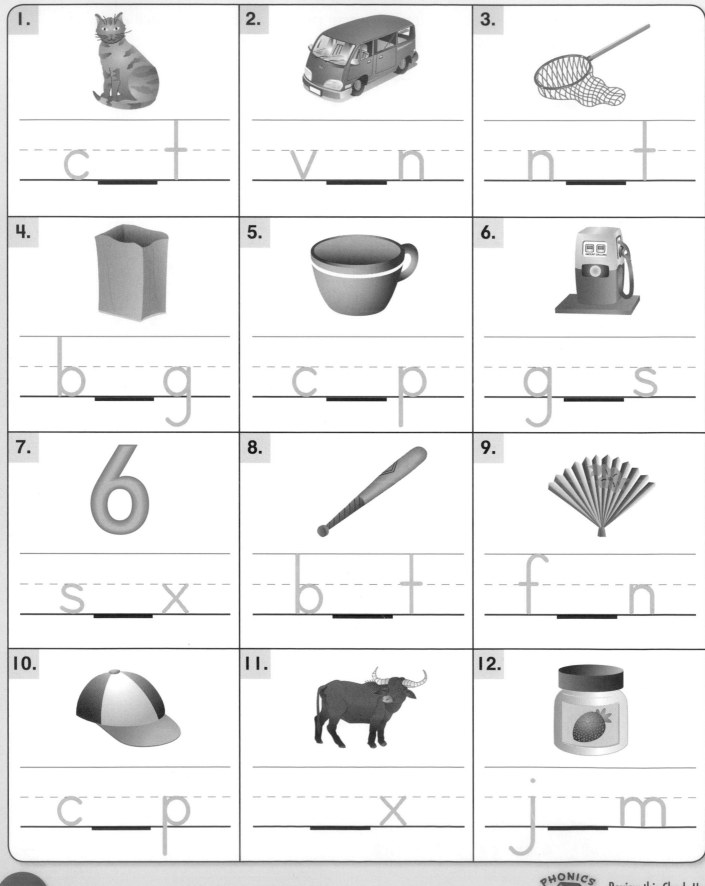

1. c _ t

2. v _ n

3. n _ t

4. b _ g

5. c _ p

6. g _ s

7. s _ x

8. b _ t

9. f _ n

10. c _ p

11. _ x

12. j _ m

PHONICS ALIVE AT HOME Review this Check-Up with your child.

Listen

Listen as the page is read aloud. **Talk** about the short **i** words you hear, such as **it** and **six**. **Draw** the answer to the riddle.

What Is It?

It has **six** legs,
and **it** has **wings.**

It is yellow and black,
and sometimes **it stings!**

What **is it?**
It is a **big**…

Oral Language What are the names of some other bugs with wings?

Sound to Symbol

Six has the short **i** sound. **Say** the name of the picture. **Print i** on the line under each picture that has the short **i** sound in its name.

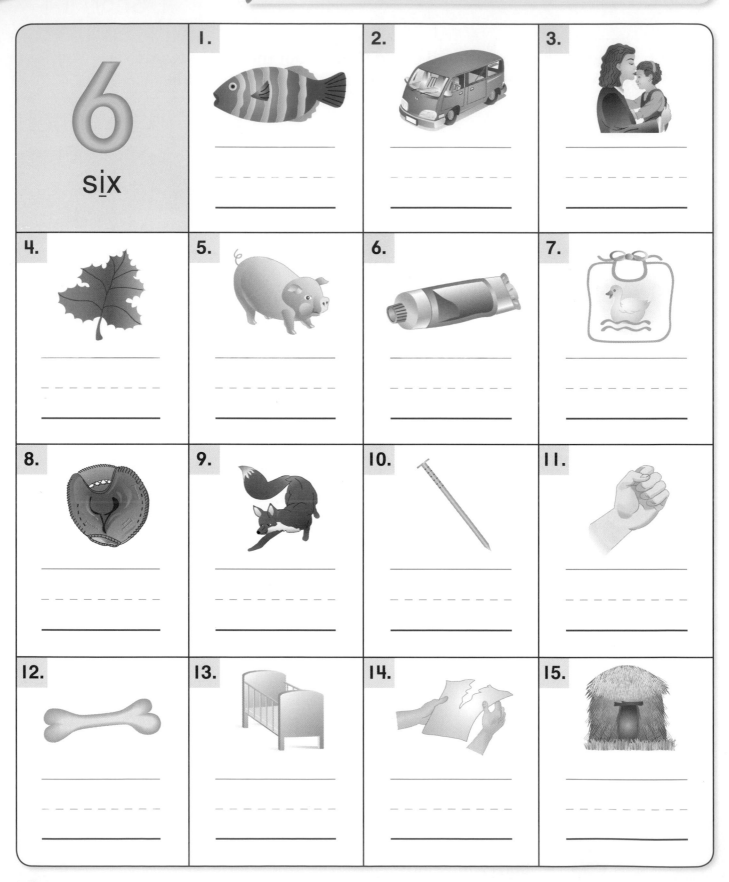

6
s i x

1.

2.

3.

4.

5.

6.

7.

8.

9.

10.

11.

12.

13.

14.

15.

PHONICS
ALIVE AT HOME

Say the name of each picture. Ask your child to hold up six fingers if the name has the short **i** sound.

Trace the line as you blend the sounds together to say the word.
Circle the picture named.

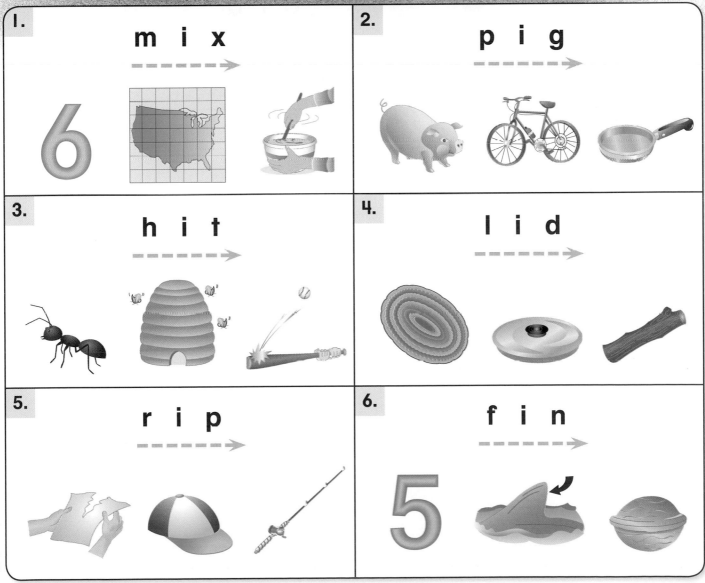

1. m i x

2. p i g

3. h i t

4. l i d

5. r i p

6. f i n

Trace the line as you blend the sounds together to say each word.
Print the word that names the picture.

I.
t i p

w i g

_____
- - - - - - -
_____

2.
p i n

d i d

_____
- - - - - - -
_____

3.
f i t

b i b

_____
- - - - - - -
_____

4.
s i x

b i g

_____
- - - - - - -
_____

5.
h i m

k i t

_____
- - - - - - -
_____

6.
z i p

w i n

_____
- - - - - - -
_____

PHONICS ALIVE AT HOME

Have your child retrace the arrow slowly with a pencil or crayon as you blend each word.

Say the name of each picture. In each row, **circle** two pictures that have rhyming names. Make a new rhyming word. **Print** it on the line.

1.

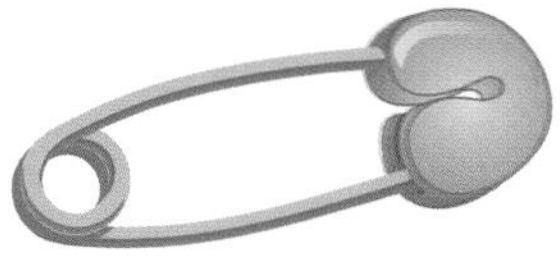

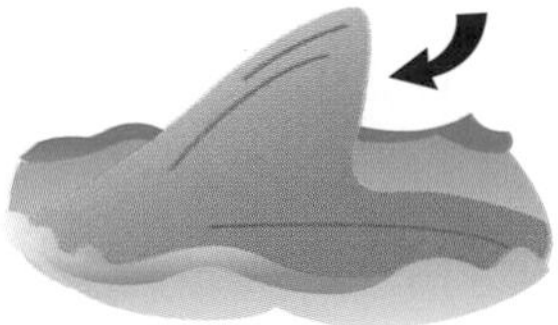

_ _ _ _ _ in

2.

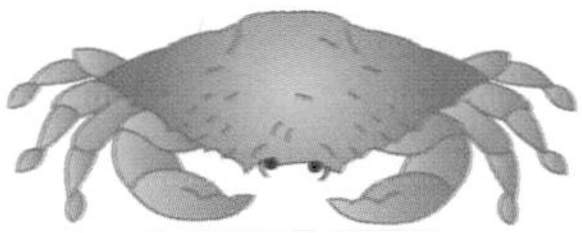

3.

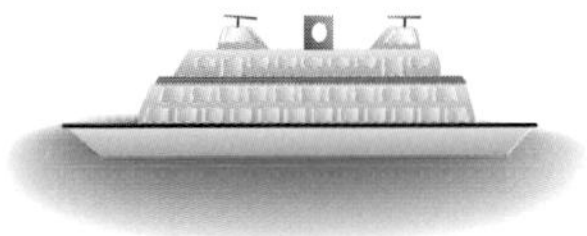

4.

5.

Trace the line as you blend the sounds together to say the word. **Print** the word on the line.

1.

f   in

_____

2.

b   ib

_____

3.

p   in

_____

4.

l   id

_____

5.

s   ix

_____

6.

w   ig

_____

7.

m   ix

_____

8.

d   ig

_____

9.

r   ip

_____

Let your child teach you how to use the arrows to blend the words on the page.

Trace the line as you blend the sounds together to say the word.
Print the word on the line. Circle the picture it names.

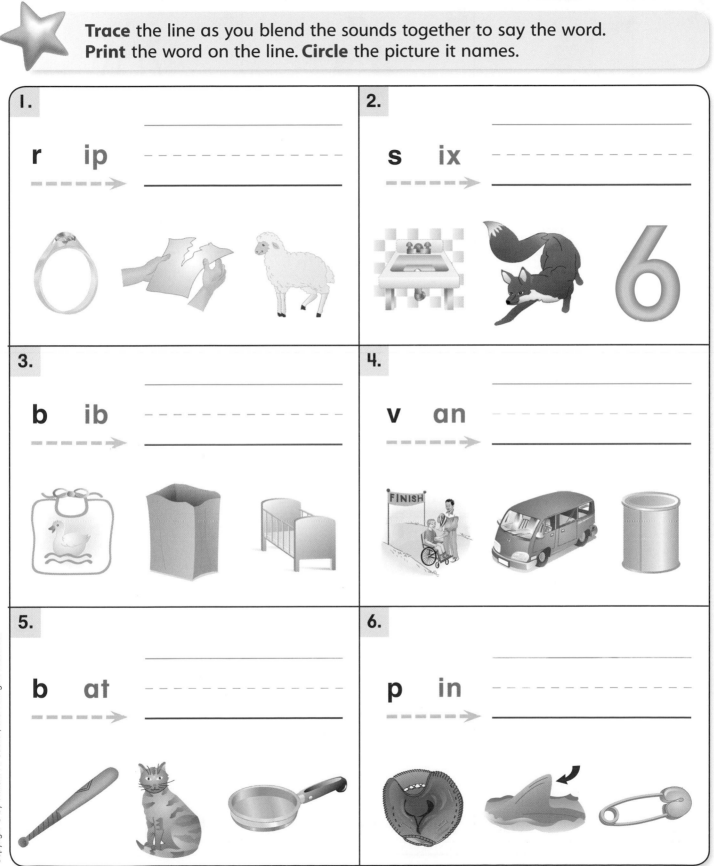

1.

r   ip _____

2.

s   ix _____

3.

b   ib _____

4.

v   an _____

5.

b   at _____

6.

p   in _____

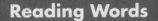

Say the name of the picture. Circle its name.

1.
win   will   tin

2.
fit   sink   six

3.
hill   gift   grill

4.
pin   fix   fin

5.
ham   hit   hat

6.
laps   sips   lips

7.
bit   fib   bib

8.
pit   pan   pin

9.
cat   bit   bat

10.
hill   will   him

11.
wag   wig   win

12.
pin   pan   pat

13.
bag   big   bug

14.
mitt   mat   milk

15.
pit   pig   wig

PHONICS ALIVE AT HOME

Read a circled word. Have your child say the word slowly, separating the initial sound from the rest of the word: **w in.**

Say the name of the picture. **Circle** its name and **print** it on the line.

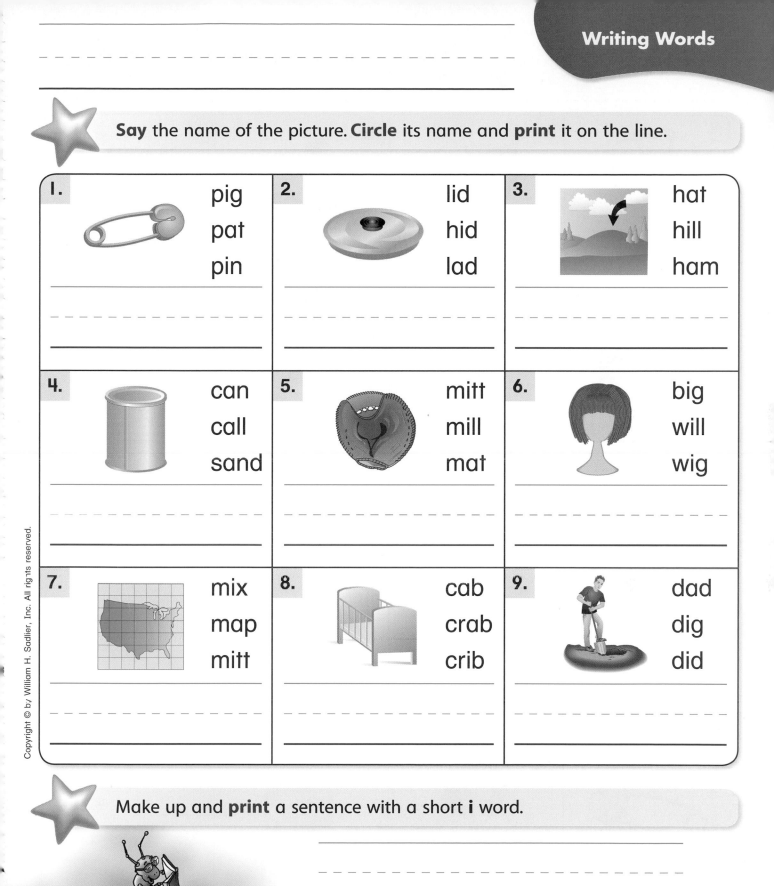

1. pig
   pat
   pin

2. lid
   hid
   lad

3. hat
   hill
   ham

4. can
   call
   sand

5. mitt
   mill
   mat

6. big
   will
   wig

7. mix
   map
   mitt

8. cab
   crab
   crib

9. dad
   dig
   did

Make up and print a sentence with a short i word.

Say the name of the picture. **Print** its name on the line.

1.	2.	3.	4.
5.	6.	7.	8.
9.	10.	11.	12.
13.	14.	15.	16.

PHONICS ALIVE AT HOME

Ask your child to read the words. Work together to make up sentences for three of the words.

Ask your child to read this book to you. Then have him or her point out the short **i** words in the story.

Read

Name _____

Fix This

Can you fix this? Can you fix this mitt?

1

8 Get in! Get in! The rip is fixed!

6 My lid! My lid is fixed!

Can you fix this? Can you fix this wig?

3

DIRECTIONS: Cut and fold the book. Read the story. If you come to a word you don't know, sound it out by looking at each letter. Tell how the problems were solved.

Lesson 52 • Short Vowel **i** Reader
Comprehension: Identifying
Problem/Solution

79

My mitt! My mitt is fixed!

2

Can you fix this? Can you fix this rip?

7

My wig! My wig is fixed!

4

Can you fix this? Can you fix this lid?

5

⭐ **Look** at the picture. **Circle** the word that completes the sentence. **Print** it on the line.

1.	Lin _____ still.	hits rips sits
2.	A bug _____ in the grass.	is kiss as
3.	Lin is _____ to grab it.	bib sink quick
4.	Lin has the bug _____ the jar.	is in it
5.	Lin looks at _____ .	it in an
6.	She lifts the _____ .	lad lid Lin

Read the poem to find out about bugs. Use short **i** words to complete the sentences.

What Is a Bug?

Some bugs have six legs,
one, two, three, four, five, six!
Some bugs have odd names,
like walkingsticks.

Insects can have wings,
and some can even sting!
It seems that bugs can do
all kinds of things.

_____
- - - - - - - - - - - - -

1. Some bugs have _____ legs.

_____
- - - - - - - - - - - -

2. Bugs with _____ can fly.

_____
- - - - - - - - - -

3. Look out for bugs that can _____ .

Lesson 53 • Short Vowel **i** in Context
Comprehension: Setting a Purpose for Reading

PHONICS
ALIVE AT HOME
Have your child use a crayon to underline short **i** words in the poem.

Read the story. **Print** three short **i** words from the story and three more short **i** words that you know. Then **read** all the words you wrote.

Jill's Jig

Will Jill win?
Jill has a big wig.
Jill has a big six.
Jill has a big pin.

What will Jill do with the big wig?
What will Jill do with the big six?
What will Jill do with the big pin?

Jill will do a jig!
Jill will win!

Story Words

1. _____

2. _____

3. _____

My Words

1. _____

2. _____

3. _____

Will Mom Fix It?

Kit has a problem with her costume. It is too big! How can Mom help? **Write** about what you see. Use some short **i** words. **Look** at the words in the box if you need help.

Kit	will	it	fix	sit
big	did	pin	if	fit

Lesson 54 • Writing Short Vowel **i** in Context

PHONICS ALIVE AT HOME Have your child read the short **i** words in the box. Ask your child to identify things around the house that have the short **i** sound in their names.

Check-Up **Say** the name of the picture. **Print i** on the line if the picture name has the short **i** sound. Then **trace** the whole word.

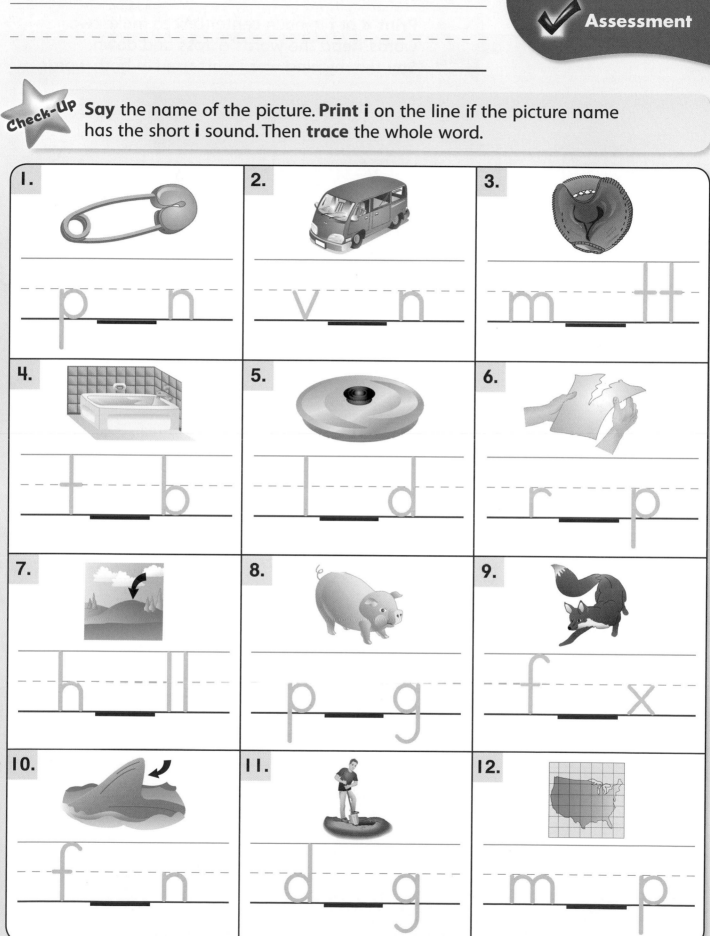

1. p _ n

2. v _ n

3. m _ tt

4. _ t _ b

5. l _ d

6. r _ p

7. h _ ll

8. p _ g

9. f _ x

10. f _ n

11. d _ g

12. m _ p

Lesson 55 • Assessing Short Vowel **i**   85

Print **a** or **i** in each center box to make two words. **Read** the words across and down. **Say** the rhyming word part used in both words.

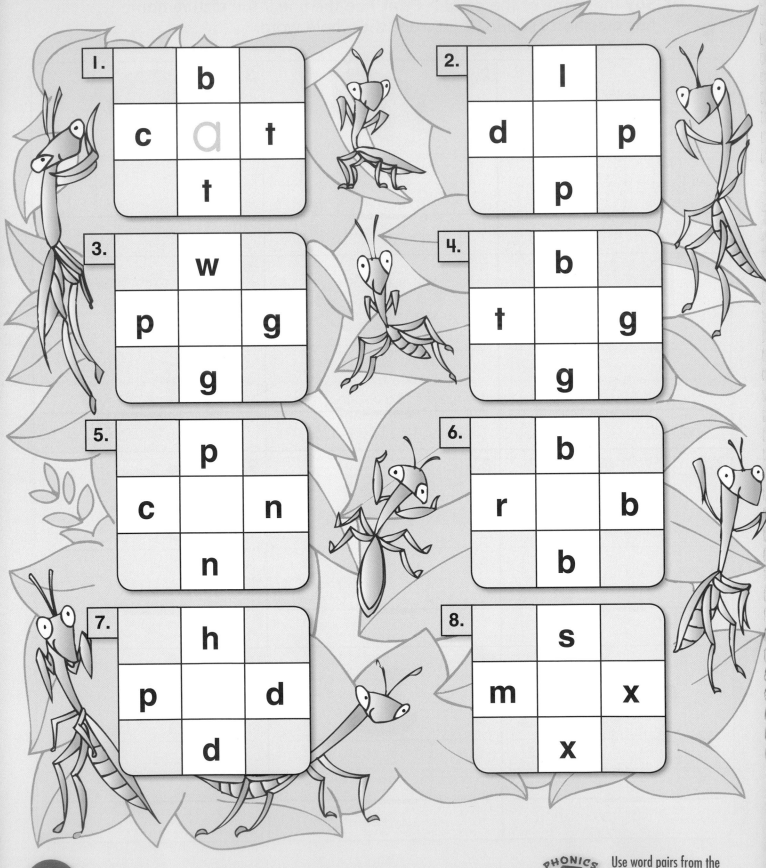

1.

	b	
c	a	t
	t	

2.

	l	
d		p
	p	

3.

	w	
p		g
	g	

4.

	b	
t		g
	g	

5.

	p	
c		n
	n	

6.

	b	
r		b
	b	

7.

	h	
p		d
	d	

8.

	s	
m		x
	x	

PHONICS ALIVE AT HOME   Use word pairs from the puzzles to make up silly rhymes with your child.

Listen as the page is read aloud. **Talk** about the short **o** words you hear, such as **hop** and **stop.** Then hop like a bug and stop like one, too.

Hop and Stop

Hop! Hop! Hop!
Time to **stop.**

Hop to the **box.**
Time to **stop.**

Jog in place.
Time to **stop.**

Isn't it fun
to **hop** and **stop?**

Oral Language What are some other ways bugs can move?

Box has the short **o** sound. **Say** the name of the picture. **Print o** on the line under each picture that has the short **o** sound in its name.

box

1.

2.

3.

4.

5.

6.

7.

8.

9.

10.

11.

12.

13.

14.

15.

 PHONICS ALIVE AT HOME   Say the name of each picture. Then have your child point to the picture of the box when he or she hears the short **o** sound.

Trace the line as you blend the sounds together to say the word.
Circle the picture named.

I.

h o p ----->

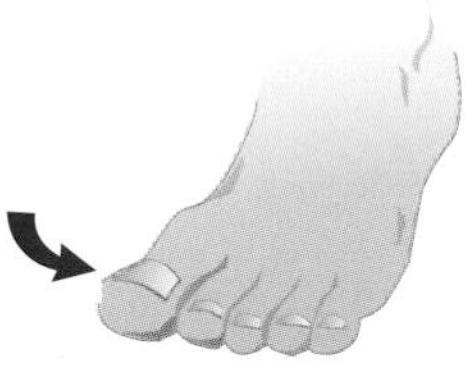

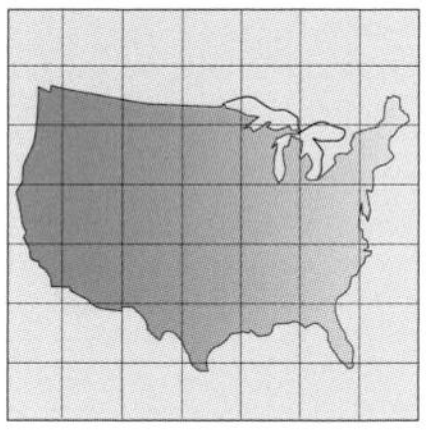

2.

f o x ----->

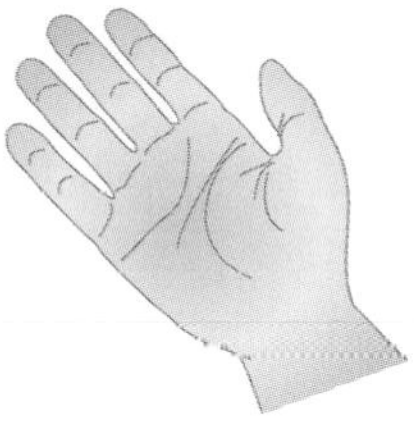

3.

l o g ----->

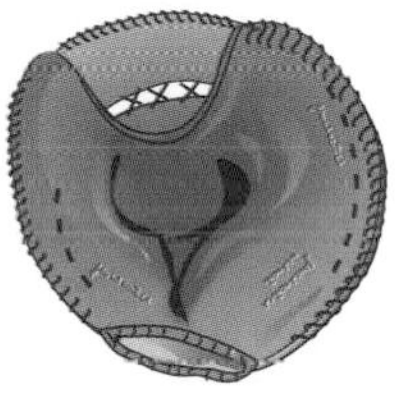

4.

r o d ----->

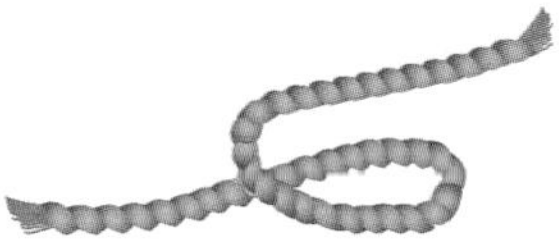

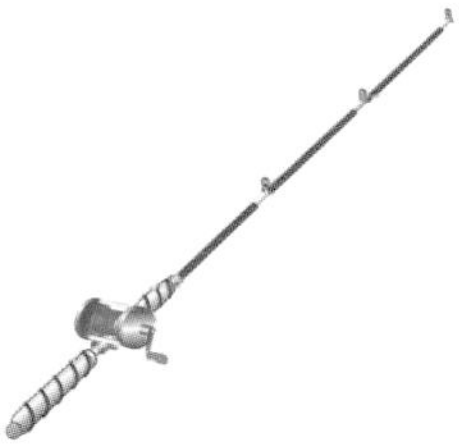

5.

h o t ----->

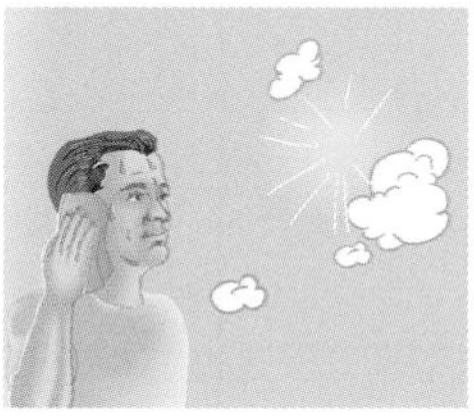

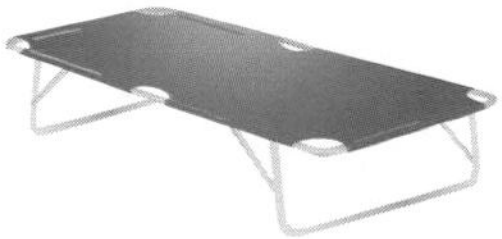

⭐ Trace the line as you blend the sounds together to say the word. **Say** the name of the picture. **Print** the word under the picture it names.

c o t   h o p   l o g

r o d   f o x   p o t

d o g   m o p   c o b

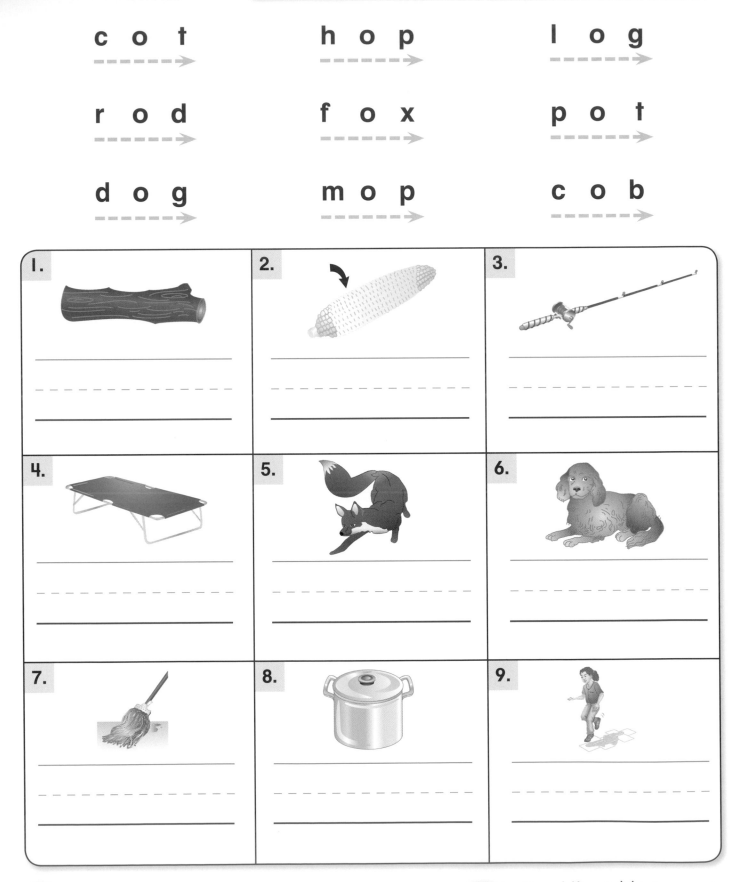

1.

2.

3.

4.

5.

6.

7.

8.

9.

PHONICS ALIVE AT HOME   Say words like **pop,** dad, **not,** mess, **mom, dog,** let, and **top.** Have your child hop when he or she hears a short **o** word.

Say the name of each picture. In each row, **circle** two pictures that have rhyming names. Make a new rhyming word. **Print** it on the line.

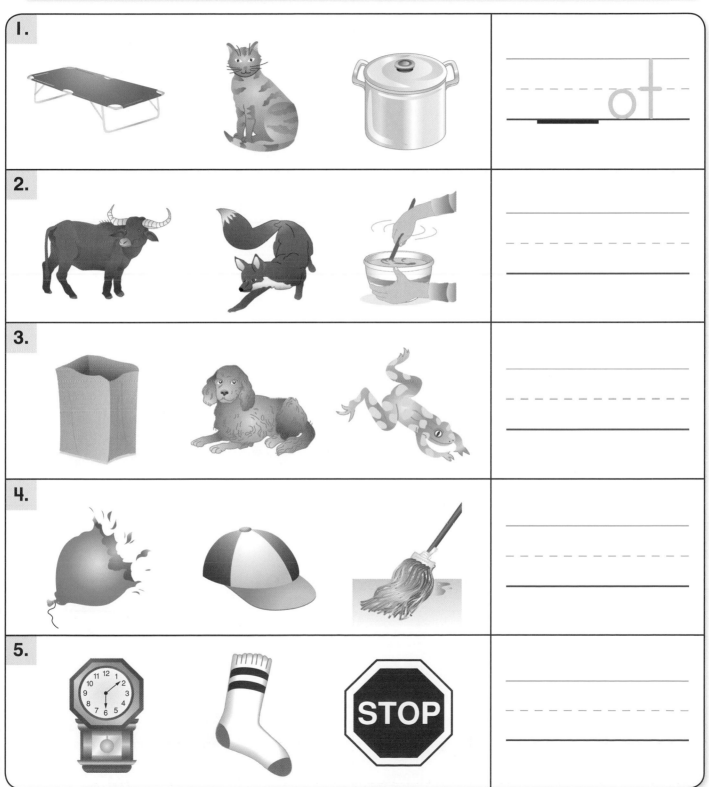

1.

o t

2.

3.

4.

5.

Trace the line as you blend the sounds together. **Print** the word on the line. **Circle** the picture it names.

1.

m op _____

2.

c ob _____

3.

p op _____

4.

b ox _____

5.

d og _____

6.

h ot _____

Lesson 58 • Blending Onsets with Short Vowel **o** Rimes

For review, have your child tell you the vowel sound in each picture name.

⬚⬚⬚⬚⬚⬚⬚⬚⬚⬚⬚⬚⬚⬚⬚⬚⬚⬚⬚⬚

Trace the line as you blend the sounds together to say the word. **Say** the name of the picture. **Print** the word under the picture it names.

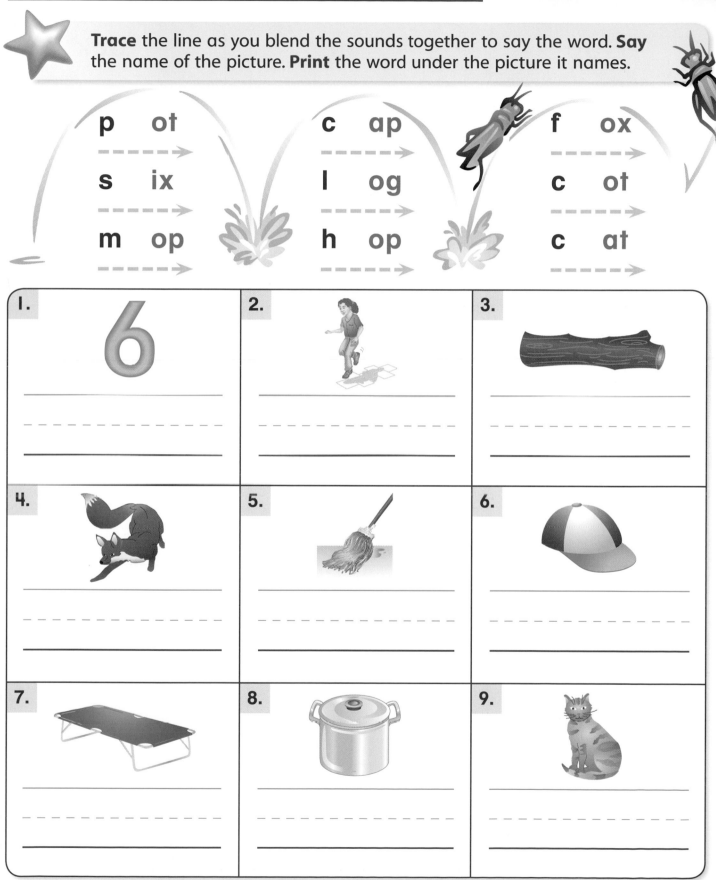

p	ot	c	ap	f	ox
s	ix	l	og	c	ot
m	op	h	op	c	at

1.

2.

3.

4.

5.

6.

7.

8.

9.

Word Building

Say the word part. **Say** the name of the picture. **Print** the word on the line. **Add** your own rhyming word and picture.

_ op

1.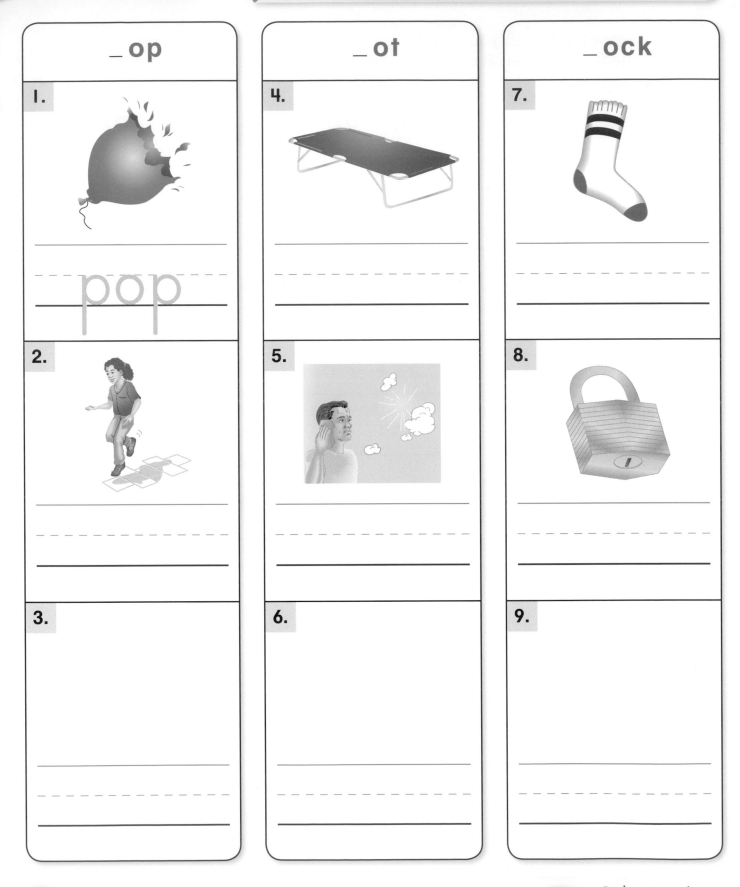

pop

2.

3.

_ ot

4.

5.

6.

_ ock

7.

8.

9.

PHONICS ALIVE AT HOME Read any two words. Have your child tell whether or not the words rhyme.

Say the name of the picture. **Circle** its name.

1. hop   mop   hip

2. log   lock   block

3. ox   fix   fox

4. pot   pond   pan

5. pit   pot   pat

6. stop   top   tip

7. hot   hat   hop

8. rock   sick   sock

9. log   dog   dig

10. mop   pop   pin

11. lock   lick   sock

12. map   hot   mop

Say the name of the picture. **Circle** its name and **print** it on the line.

1.
rock
back
lock

_____

2.
tap
tip
box

_____

3.
pit
pop
mop

_____

4.
cob
cat
cot

_____

5.
wig
wag
win

_____

6.
fog
dig
frog

_____

7.
box
map
mop

_____

8.
rock
sock
rack

_____

9.
mop
man
mat

_____

Make up and **print** a sentence with a short **o** word.

_____

_____

_____

PHONICS ALIVE AT HOME

Have your child read the sentence and name the short **o** word in it.

"Do not jog," said Tom.
"Run, run, run!" said Bob.

8

"Stop, Bob, stop!"
said Tom.

6

Read

Name _____

Jog with Me

Tom likes to jog.
"Jog with me," said Tom.

1

Fold

"No, let's both jog," said Tom.
"We will jog by this log."

3

Fold

DIRECTIONS: Cut and fold the book. Read the story. If you come to a word you don't know, sound it out by looking at each letter. Tell what happens to the bugs in the book.

Lesson 61 • Short Vowel **o** Reader
Comprehension:
Summarizing

97

"I will walk," said Bob. "I will
2 walk and you can jog."

"I do not like what I see,"
said Tom. 7

"We will jog past this funny
4 dog," said Tom.

"We will jog past this pig with
a mop," said Tom. 5

Lesson 61 • Short Vowel **o** Reader
Comprehension: Summarizing

_____

- - - - - - - - - - - - - - - -

_____

Look at the picture. **Print** the correct sentence part on the line.

| on the log.   on the rock.   in the sock.   in the box.   on the dog. |

1.	Where is the bug? It is _on the dog._
2.	Where is the bug? It is _____
3.	Where is the bug? It is _____
4.	Where is the bug? It is _____
5.	Where is the bug? It is _____

Read

Read the poem. **Look** at the picture. **Number** the sentences at the bottom to show the correct order.

Hop, Bug, Hop!

Hop, Bug, hop!
1. Hop right past Pop.
2. Hop over the blocks.
3. Hop into the box.
4. Hop over the dog.
5. Hop up on the log.

Stop, Bug, stop!
Or you'll hop in the pond.

_____ The bug hops over the dog.

_____ The bug hops over the blocks.

__1__ The bug hops right past Pop.

_____ The bug hops up on the log.

_____ The bug hops into the box.

PHONICS ALIVE AT HOME
Read the story aloud. Stop before the last word in each line to let your child say the short **o** word.

Read the story. **Print** three short **o** words from the story and three more short **o** words that you know. Then **read** all the words you wrote.

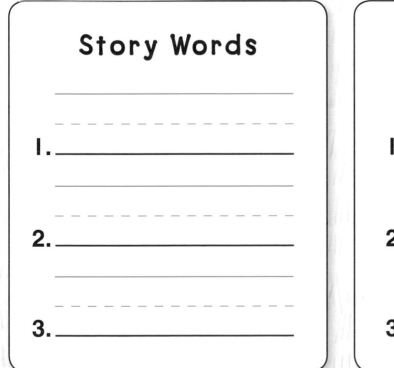

Hop, Pop!

Hop, Pop, hop!
Can Pop hop by Tom?
Pop can!
Can Pop hop by Rob?
Pop can!
Can Pop hop by Don?
Pop can!
Can Pop hop by Mom?
Pop can not!

Story Words

1._____

2._____

3._____

My Words

1._____

2._____

3._____

A Hot Pot!

Bob the Bug is making something in his pot. **Write** about it. Use some short **o** words. **Look** at the words in the box if you need help.

Bob	hot	pot	pop	mom
mop	hop	lot	top	got

PHONICS ALIVE AT HOME Have your child read the short **o** words in the box. Note any words he or she has trouble reading. Ask your child to read those words again.

Check-Up **Say** the name of the picture. **Print o** on the line if the picture name has the short **o** sound. Then **trace** the whole word.

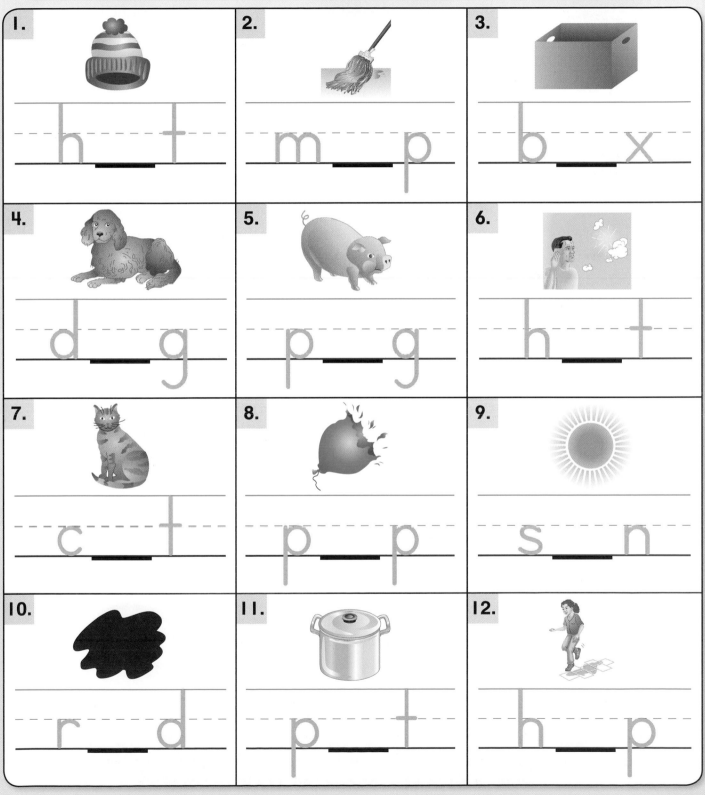

1. h _ t

2. m _ p

3. b _ x

4. d _ g

5. p _ g

6. h _ t

7. c _ t

8. p _ p

9. s _ n

10. r _ d

11. p _ t

12. h _ p

Color the box that contains the short vowel sound in the picture name. **Write** the vowel to complete the word. Then **trace** the whole word.

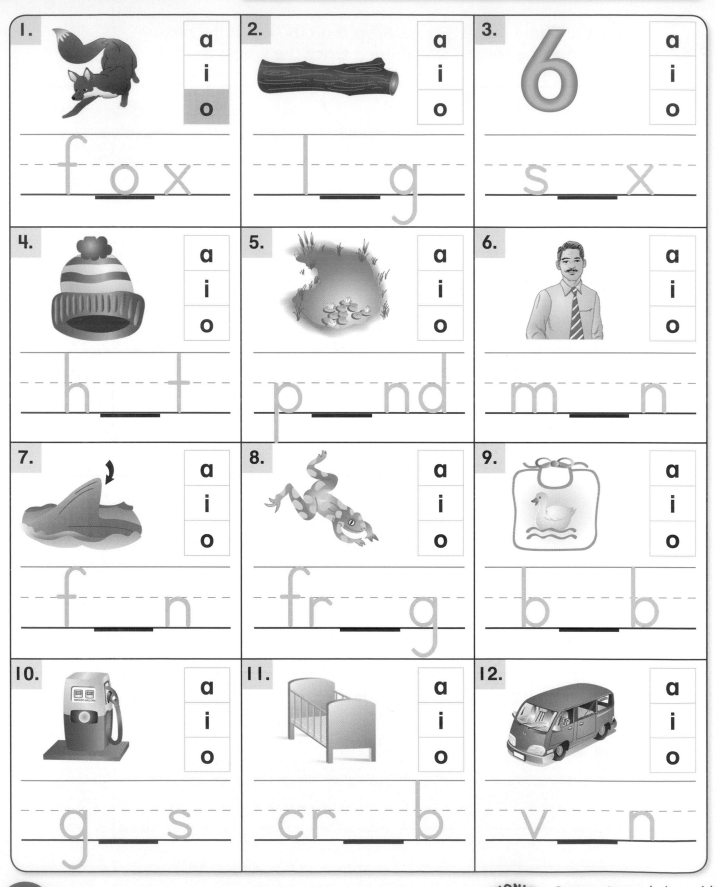

1. a i **o**

f o x

2. a i o

l _ g

3. a i o

s _ x

4. a i o

h _ t

5. a i o

p _ nd

6. a i o

m _ n

7. a i o

f _ n

8. a i o

fr _ g

9. a i o

b _ b

10. a i o

g _ s

11. a i o

cr _ b

12. a i o

v _ n

PHONICS ALIVE AT HOME Point to a picture and ask your child to tell you the vowel sound.

Check-Up Say the name of the picture. Circle its name and print it on the line.

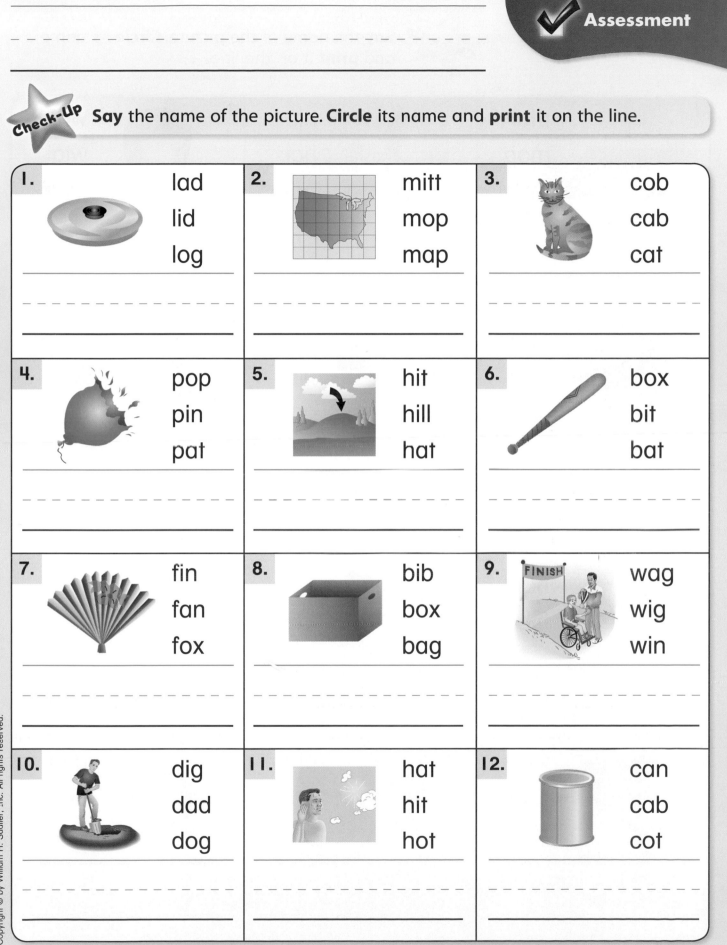

1.
lad
lid
log

2.
mitt
mop
map

3.
cob
cab
cat

4.
pop
pin
pat

5.
hit
hill
hat

6.
box
bit
bat

7.
fin
fan
fox

8.
bib
box
bag

9.
wag
wig
win

FINISH

10.
dig
dad
dog

11.
hat
hit
hot

12.
can
cab
cot

Check-Up **Say** the name of the picture. **Circle** its name and **print** it on the line.

1.
WELCOME

mat
mop
mitt

_____

2.

hip
hop
ham

_____

3.

wax
wig
wag

_____

4.

cot
cat
can

_____

5.

pop
pin
pan

_____

6.
6

six
fox
sat

_____

7.

cob
bat
bib

_____

8.

lap
pig
log

_____

9.
25¢

top
tag
wig

_____

10.

fix
fox
fan

_____

11.

pig
bag
pot

_____

12.

can
cap
cot

_____

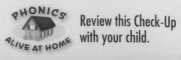 **PHONICS ALIVE AT HOME** Review this Check-Up with your child.

Listen

Listen as the page is read aloud. **Talk** about the short **u** words you hear, such as **bug** and **rug**. **Color** the bugs.

A Snug Bug

One little **bug**
in the middle of a **rug**.
Poor little **bug**
isn't very **snug**.

Tug, bug, tug!
Roll up the **rug**.
Soon you'll be all
cozy and **snug**.

Oral Language Where else would a bug feel cozy and snug?

Bug has the short **u** sound. **Say** the name of the picture. **Print u** on the line under each picture that has the short **u** sound in its name.

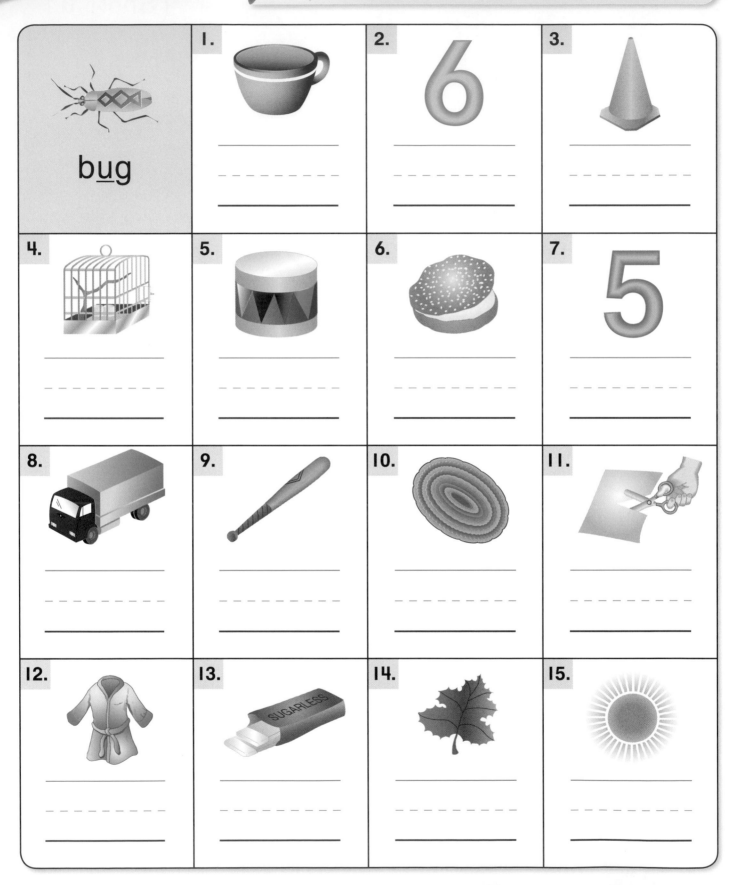

bug

1.

2.

3.

4.

5.

6.

7.

8.

9.

10.

11.

12.

13.

14.

15.

PHONICS ALIVE AT HOME

Name the pictures on the page. Have your child drum on a table when he or she hears a word with the short **u** sound.

Trace the line as you blend the sounds together to say the word.
Say the name of each picture. Circle the picture named.

1.

t u b

2.

s u n

3.

c u p

4.

m u d

5.

n u t

6.

b u g

25¢

Blending Phonemes

Trace the line as you blend the sounds together to say each word.
Say the name of the picture. Print the word that names the picture.

1. h u t
   t u g

2. g u m
   b u n

3. c u p
   b u s

4. b u d
   j u g

5. r u n
   d u g

6. h u m
   c u b

PHONICS
ALIVE AT HOME

Say the three sounds in each word, for example, c-u-p. Have your child put a penny in a cup for each sound.

Say the name of each picture. In each row, **circle** two pictures that have rhyming names. Make a new rhyming word. **Print** it on the line.

1.

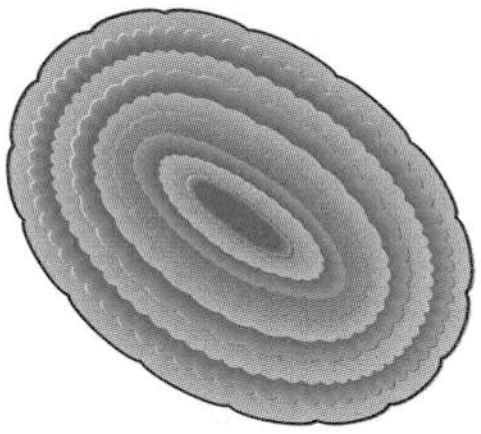

_____ ug

2.

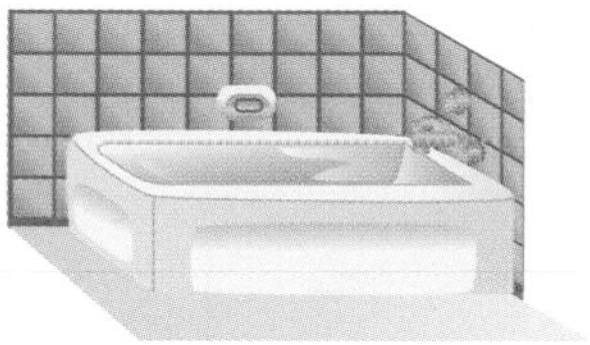

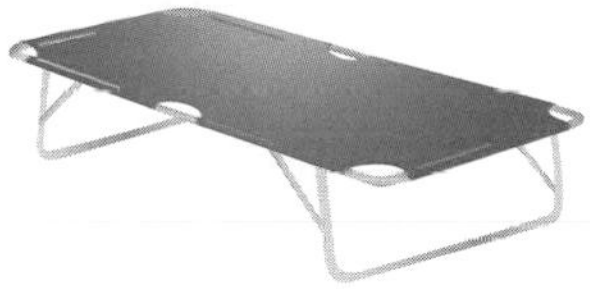

3.

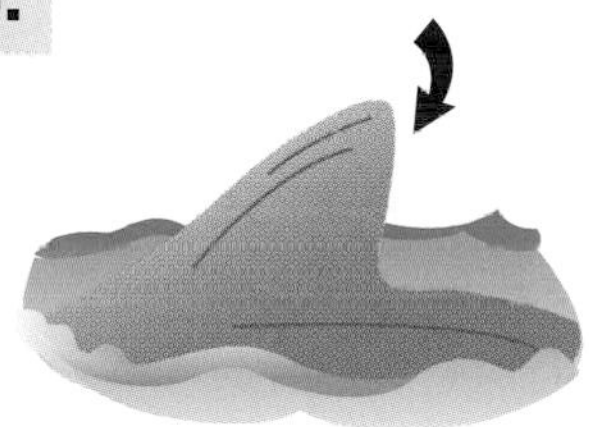

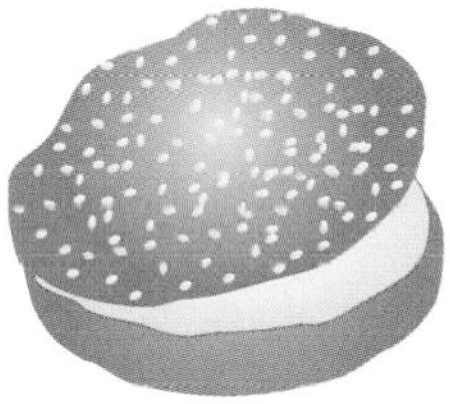

4.

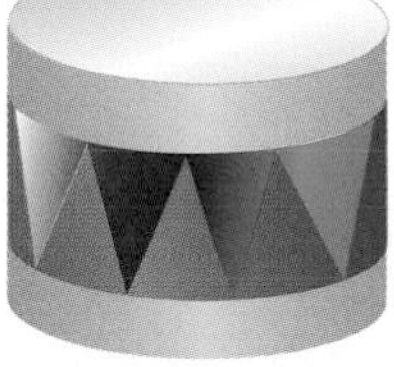

5.

Trace the line as you blend the sounds together to say the word. **Say** the name of the picture. **Print** the word on the line.

1. c ub

2. h ut

3. p up

4. b us

5. b un

6. n ut

7. r ug

8. c up

9. h ug

PHONICS ALIVE AT HOME

Trace the arrow slowly with your finger as your child blends each word.

Trace the line as you blend the sounds together to say the word.
Print the word on the line. **Circle** the picture it names.

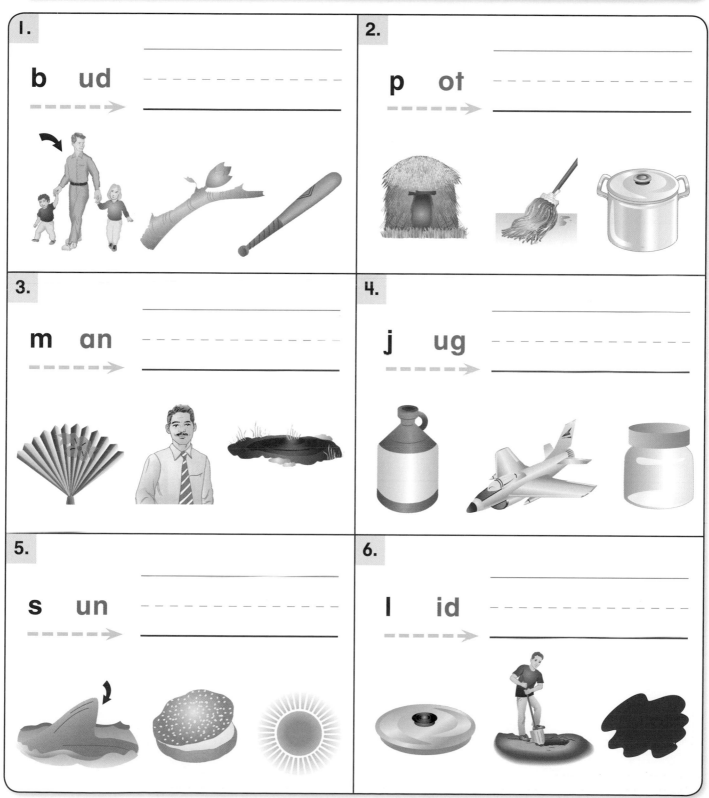

1.

b   ud

2.

p   ot

3.

m   an

4.

j   ug

5.

s   un

6.

l   id

Say the word part. **Say** the name of the picture. **Print** the word on the line. **Add** your own rhyming word and picture.

_ ug

1.

2.

3.

_ un

4.

5.

6.

_ ut

7.

8.

9.

Lesson 69 • Word Building with Short Vowel **u**
Word Families

PHONICS ALIVE AT HOME

Cut out the boxes and turn them over. With your child, take turns choosing two pictures. If the two picture names rhyme, read them aloud.

⭐ **Say** the name of the picture. **Circle** its name.

1.	2.	3.
pop pup cup	dad did dud	jig jog jug
4.	5.	6.
bug bag big	mat mutt mitt	cob cub cab
7.	8.	9.
pot pat putt	mud bad bud	nut not hut
10.	11.	12.
rig rag rug	cap cup cut	hug hog hut
13.	14.	15.
cub tub tab	cut cat cot	bit but bat

Writing Words

Say the name of the picture. **Circle** its name and **print** it on the line.

1.	tub	2.	bit	3.	nut
	cub		bad		cut
	cob		bun		not

4.	and	5.	bus	6.	hill
	fun		bug		hot
	fan		gas		hit

7.	sun	8.	pig	9.	gum
	run		log		bug
	ran		pup		big

Make up and **print** a sentence with a short **u** word.

116 Lesson 70 • Writing Short Vowel **u**

PHONICS ALIVE AT HOME

Point to each picture on the page. Have your child use each picture name in a sentence.

Ask your child to read this book to you. Then have him or her point out the short **u** words in the story.

Read

Name _____

Gus and Mom

Mom is up, but Gus is not.
Gus is very hot.

1

Now Gus is up, but Mom
is not. Mom is very tired.

8

Mom gives Gus a big hug.
Feel better, Gus.

6

Mom gives Gus his little pup.
Feel better, Gus.

3

DIRECTIONS: Cut and fold the book. Read the story. If you come to a word you don't know, sound it out by looking at each letter. Tell where the story happens.

Lesson 71 • Short Vowel **u** Reader
Comprehension: Identifying
the Setting

117

Mom gives Gus a cup of
2 soup. Feel better, Gus.

Gus starts to cheer up.
Gus feels much better.   7

Mom fills up the tub for Gus.
4 Feel better, Gus.

Mom cuts a yellow bus for Gus.
Feel better, Gus.   5

Look at the picture. **Circle** the word that completes the sentence. **Print** it on the line.

1.	The _____ naps in the sun.	pup pep pop
2.	"Buzz," _____ the bug.	has hams hums
3.	The pup looks _____ at it.	us up as
4.	It bats at the _____ .	bag beg bug
5.	This is not _____ .	fit fun fat
6.	The pup _____ off.	runs suns buns

Read **Read** the poem to find out about bugs. Use short **u** words to complete the sentences.

A Buggy Lunch

A bug is in my cup.
A bug is on my bun.
A bug is by my pup.
Run, bugs, run!

Run, bugs, run.
Please do not munch
on our lunch.

1. A bug is in my _____ .

2. A bug is on my _____ .

3. A bug is by my _____ .

4. Do not _____ on our lunch.

Lesson 72 • Short Vowel **u** in Context
Comprehension: Recalling Details

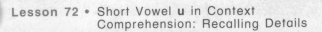

PHONICS ALIVE AT HOME   Read the poem with your child.
Then ask him or her to repeat
all of the short **u** words.

Phonics in Context

Read the story. **Print** three short **u** words from the story and three more short **u** words that you know. Then **read** all the words you wrote.

The Rug

The bug has a rug.
The bug will lug the rug
to his hut.
But the sun is hot.
This is NOT fun!

The bug can see a bus.
The bug can ride on the bus.
The bug will lug the rug on the bus.

This is fun!

Story Words

1._____

2._____

3._____

My Words

1._____

2._____

3._____

Copyright © by William H. Sadlier, Inc. All rights reserved.

Lesson 73 • Reading Short Vowel **u** in Context **121**

Mud! Mud! Mud!

It is a hot day. The pups find ways to stay cool. **Write** about what you see. Use some short **u** words. **Look** at the words in the box if you need help.

pup	mud	tub	fun	gum
mug	cup	run	jug	sun

PHONICS ALIVE AT HOME Have your child read the short **u** words in the box. Then ask your child to make a list of other short **u** words while you make your own list. Then compare your lists.

Check-Up **Say** the name of the picture. **Print u** on the line if the picture name has the short **u** sound. Then **trace** the whole word.

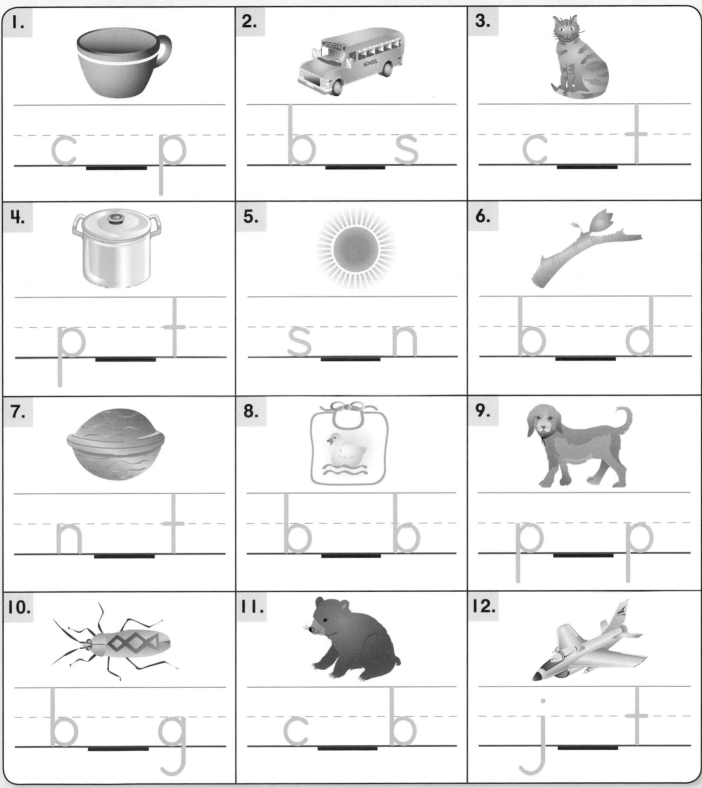

1. c ___ p

2. b ___ s

3. c ___ t

4. p ___ t

5. s ___ n

6. b ___ d

7. n ___ t

8. b ___ b

9. p ___ p

10. b ___ g

11. c ___ b

12. j ___ t

Find six hidden short vowel words. **Circle** them. **Print** the vowel to complete each word. Then **trace** the whole word.

b	a	t	r	u	g
r	p	l	d	e	p
u	n	r	i	s	e
n	t	a	g	i	c
h	o	p	e	x	d

1. b a t

2. r _ g

3. h _ p

4. r _ n

5. s _ x

6. t _ g

PHONICS ALIVE AT HOME   Read aloud the words your child circled. Ask him or her to name the short vowel in each word.

Listen as the page is read aloud. **Talk** about the short **e** words you hear, such as **Ted** and **mess.** **Name** the things under the bed. **Color** them Ted's favorite color—red.

Ted's Room

It's **Ted,** the bug.
His room's a **mess.**
He has **ten** things
no more, no **less.**

He hid his things
under his **bed.**
And all the things
Ted hid are **red.**

Oral Language What should Ted do to make his room look better?

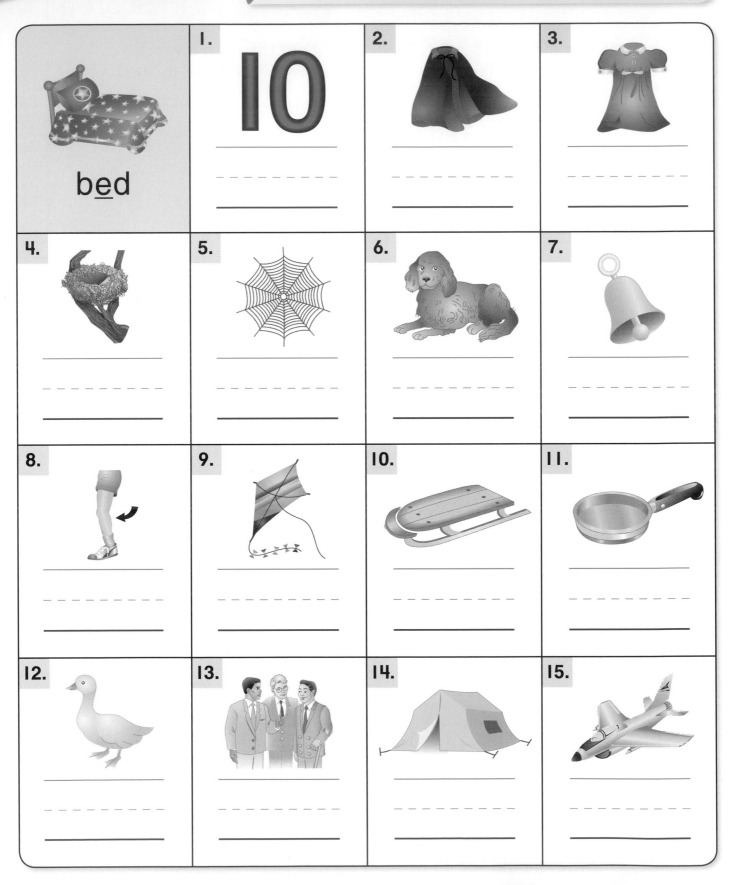

Bed has the short **e** sound. **Say** the name of the picture. **Print e** on the line under each picture that has the short **e** sound in its name.

bed

Randomly name the pictures on the page. Have your child bend if the picture name has the short e sound.

Trace the line as you blend the sounds together to say the word.
Circle the picture named.

1.

w e b

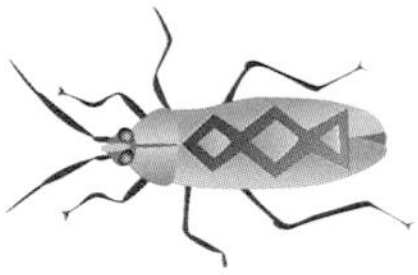

2.

b e g

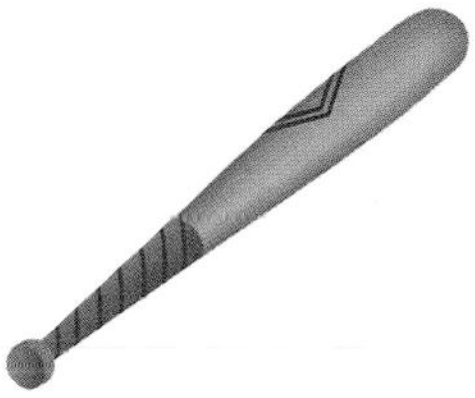

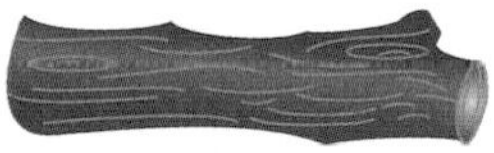

3.

r e d

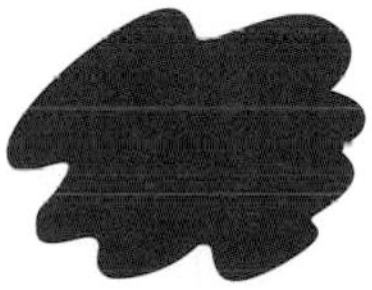

4.

j e t

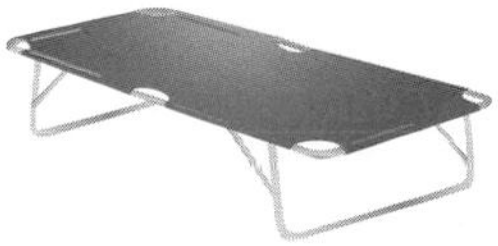

5.

p e n

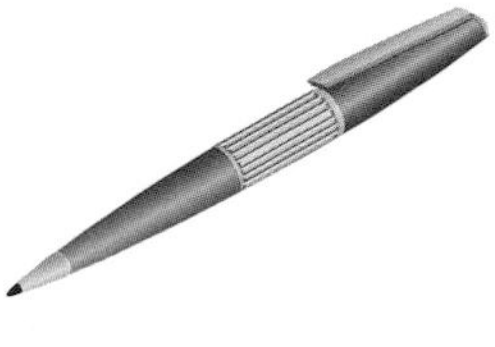

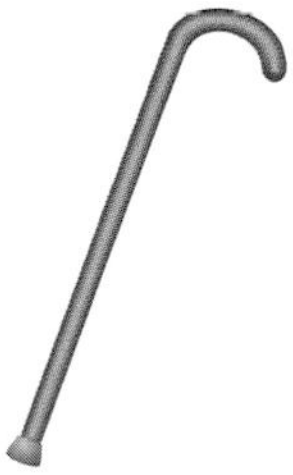

Trace the line as you blend the sounds together to say the word. **Say** the name of the picture. **Print** the word under the picture it names.

p e t

h e n

w e b

m e n

l e g

v e t

b e d

n e t

t e n

1.

2.

3.

4.

5.

6.

7.

8. 10

9.

PHONICS ALIVE AT HOME   As your child blends each word, slowly retrace the arrow with a pen or crayon.

> ⭐ **Say** the name of each picture. In each row, **circle** two pictures that have rhyming names. Make a new rhyming word. **Print** it on the line.

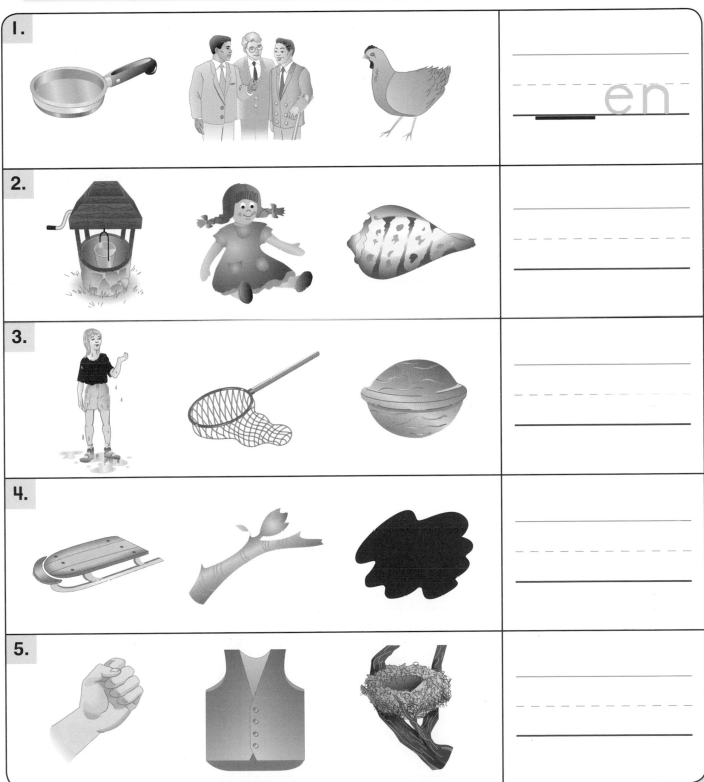

1. _____ en

2.

3.

4.

5.

Blending Onsets and Rimes

1. h en _____

2. p et _____

3. b ed _____

4. n et _____

5. m en _____

6. l eg _____

Say the first sound of each word on this page. Have your child say the rest of the word. Then say the whole word together.

Trace the line as you blend the sounds together to say the word.
Say the name of the picture. **Print** the word under the picture it names.

v   et

w   ell

r   ed

w   eb

n   est

b   eg

t   en

b   ell

j   et

1.

2.

3.

4. **10**

5.

6.

7.

8.

9.

Word Building

_ en

1.

2

3.

_ et

4.

5.

6.

_ ell

7.

8.

9.

PHONICS
ALIVE AT HOME

With your child, use two words from any column in a short rhyme like this: **Yell for a shell.**

⭐ **Say** the name of the picture. **Circle** its name.

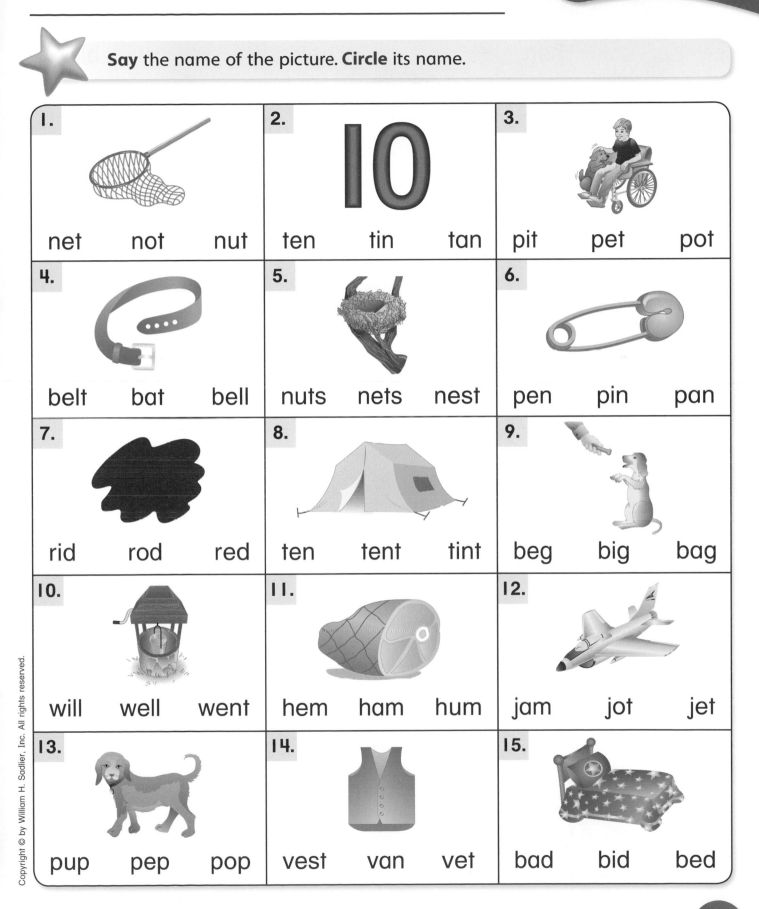

1. net not nut	**2.** ten tin tan	**3.** pit pet pot
4. belt bat bell	**5.** nuts nets nest	**6.** pen pin pan
7. rid rod red	**8.** ten tent tint	**9.** beg big bag
10. will well went	**11.** hem ham hum	**12.** jam jot jet
13. pup pep pop	**14.** vest van vet	**15.** bad bid bed

Say the name of the picture. **Circle** the name of the picture and **print** it on the line.

1.
hen
den
dim
_____
_____

2.
net
rut
nut
_____
_____

3.
bill
bull
bell
_____
_____

4.
10
ten
tent
tin
_____
_____

5.
disk
desk
dent
_____
_____

6.
wet
will
well
_____
_____

7.
bag
leg
let
_____
_____

8.
man
met
men
_____
_____

9.
bit
bat
bet
_____
_____

Make up and **print** a sentence with a short **e** word.

_____
_____
_____
_____

PHONICS ALIVE AT HOME Randomly read words on this page. Have your child hold up ten fingers when he or she hears a short **e** word.

Name _____

Yes It Can

Can this bug jump far?
You bet!

8

Can this bug get wet?
Yes, it can get wet.

1

Can this bug be a pet?
Yes, it can be a pet.

6

Is this bug black and red?
Yes, it is black and red.

3

DIRECTIONS: Cut and fold the book. Read the story. If you come to a word you don't know, sound it out by looking at each letter. Talk about things that are wet, red, or in a net.

Lesson 80 • Short Vowel **e** Reader
Comprehension:
Classifying Objects

135

Is this bug in a net?
2 Yes, it is in a net.

Can this bug buzz by Jen?
Yes, it can buzz by Jen. 7

Is this bug getting fed?
4 Yes, it is getting fed.

Does this bug dig with its
legs? Yes, it digs. 5

Look at the picture. **Circle** the word that completes the sentence.
Print it on the line.

1.

Can a bug be a _____ ?

pat
pet
pot

2.

_____ , it can.

Yes
Yet
Jet

3.

It can be the _____ pet.

list
best
rest

4.

It will not be a _____ .

last
past
pest

5.

It will not make a _____ .

mess
miss
moss

6.

But it must be _____ .

fan
fin
fed

Read the poem. **Circle** each thing the bugs run past. Use short **e** words to complete the sentences.

The Big Bug Race

Get set, bugs.
First, run past the hen.
Next, run past the pen.
Then, run past the men.
Run, bugs, run.
Run to the very end!

_____
- - - - - - - - - - - - - - - - -

1. The bugs run past the _____ .

_____
- - - - - - - - - - - - - - - - -

2. They run past the _____ .

_____
- - - - - - - - - - - - - - - - -

3. They run past the _____ .

_____
- - - - - - - - - - - - - - - - -

4. They run to the _____ .

138 Lesson 81 • Short Vowel **e** in Context
Comprehension: Retelling a Story

PHONICS ALIVE AT HOME

Have your child walk through your home and draw or say things he or she sees that have short e names.

> **Read** the story. **Print** three short **e** words from the story and three more short **e** words that you know. Then **read** all the words you wrote.

Ned and His Red Hen

Ned has a lot of pep.
His red hen has a lot of pep, too.
Ned can run.
His red hen can run, too.
Ned can dig.
His red hen can dig, too.
Ned can jump.
His red hen can jump, too.

Ned will nap.
His red hen will nap, too.
You can bet on that!

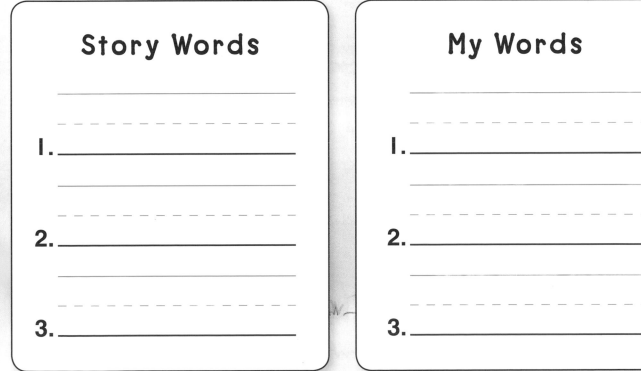

Story Words	My Words
1._____	1._____
2._____	2._____
3._____	3._____

A Wet, Wet Hen!

The hen and her eggs are getting wet! **Write** about what you see.
Use some short **e** words. **Look** at the words in the box if you need help.

hen	pen	get	wet	ten
eggs	tell	red	let	yell

PHONICS ALIVE AT HOME   Have your child read what he or she wrote. Then ask your child to circle all the short e words in his or her writing.

Check-Up **Say** the name of the picture. **Print e** on the line if the picture name has the short **e** sound. Then **trace** the whole word.

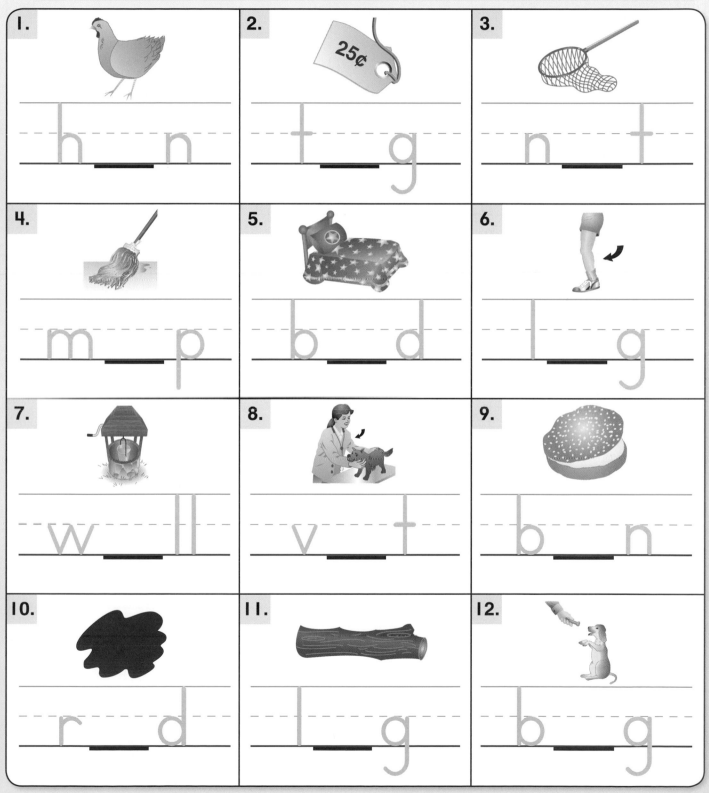

1.	2.	3.
h __ n	t __ g	n __ t
4.	5.	6.
m __ p	b __ d	l __ g
7.	8.	9.
w __ ll	v __ t	b __ n
10.	11.	12.
r __ d	l __ g	b __ g

Read the words in the boxes. **Combine** words from boxes 1, 2, and 3 to make sentences. **Print** them on the lines. How many can you make?

1.	2.	3.
Six bugs	had fun	at the pond.
A frog	will jump	in the sun.
The pet	can hop	on the bud.

A frog can hop in the sun.

Visit **www.sadlierphonicsonline.com** for another short vowel activity.

Spell, Write, and Tell **Say, spell,** and **talk** about each word in the box. **Print** each word under the vowel sound in its name.

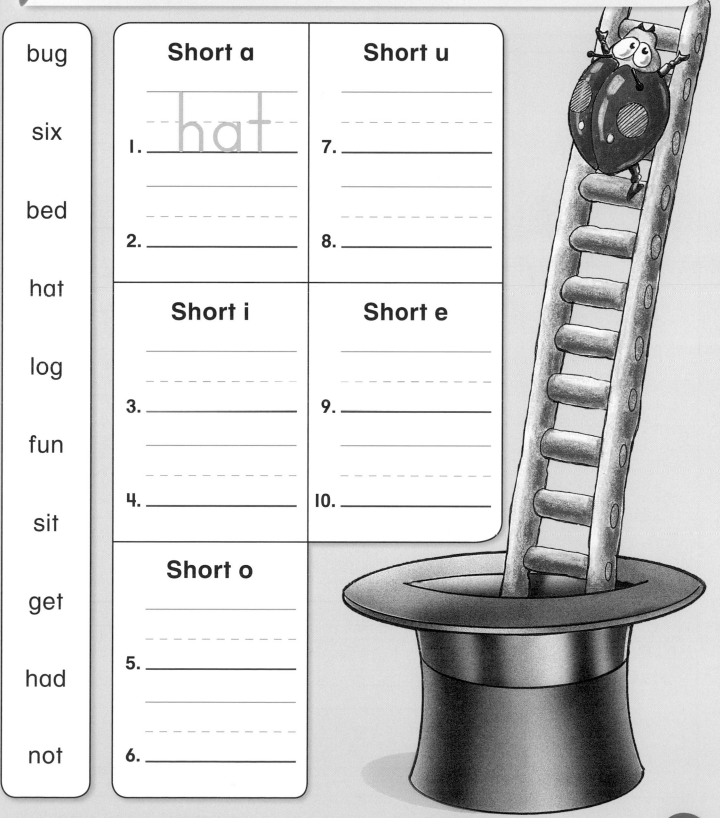

bug

six

bed

hat

log

fun

sit

get

had

not

Short a

1. hat

2. ___

Short u

7. ___

8. ___

Short i

3. ___

4. ___

Short e

9. ___

10. ___

Short o

5. ___

6. ___

Spell, Write, and Tell **Write** a sentence about each picture. Use one or more of the words in the box in each sentence. **Share** what you wrote.

bug	bed	log	sit	had
six	hat	fun	get	not

1.

2.

Take turns reading the spelling words with your child. Then have him or her spell each word.

Read Use one of the words in the box to complete each sentence. Practice **reading** the sentences aloud.

| and | help | it | No | see | will |

1.

Do you _____ a bug by the 🌳 ?

2.

Is _____ on the 🌼 ?

3.

_____ , that bug is by the 🏰 .

4.

You can _____ me stop that bug.

5.

I _____ run with you.

6.

You _____ I will get that bug!

Visit **www.sadlierphonicsonline.com** to do this activity online.

Circle the word in the box that completes each sentence. **Print** the word on the line. **Read** the sentences.

1.

_____

I _____ mud in the tub.

| see |
| walk |

2.

_____

Can you see _____ , too?

| like |
| it |

3.

_____

I will run _____ get the mop.

| and |
| can |

4.

_____

I will _____ with the mess.

| help |
| funny |

5.

_____

I _____ get in the tub!

| will |
| no |

Check-Up   **Color** a 🙂 for each word you wrote.

🙂 will   🙂 no   🙂 can   🙂 help   🙂 walk

🙂 see   🙂 it   🙂 like   🙂 and   🙂 funny

PHONICS ALIVE AT HOME   Have your child make up sentences that use the words in the Check-Up box.

READ Look at the pictures. **Read** the page. **Talk** about what you see.

Learn About Bugs

Can you spot the bugs?
Don't let them trick you.
They can see you just fine.
Lots of bugs blend in well with
rocks, plants, and sticks.
The bugs can sit still for a very
long time. This helps them hide
and stay safe.

What can bugs do?

Treehopper

Walkingstick

Katydid

Lesson 86 • Short Vowels in Context
Comprehension: Recognizing Facts
Modeling Fluency

Dig, Pat, Dig!

Pat the Pirate digs for a buried treasure chest. **Write** about what you see. Use some short vowel words. **Look** at the words in the box if you need help.

map	can	dig	will	log
hot	sun	bug	wet	ten

PHONICS ALIVE AT HOME

Have your child read what he or she wrote. Then say **hat** and ask your child to point to and read a word from the box with the same short vowel sound. Repeat with **pig**, **hop**, **tub**, and **vet**.

Check-Up **Say** the name of the picture. **Fill in** the circle next to the name of the picture.

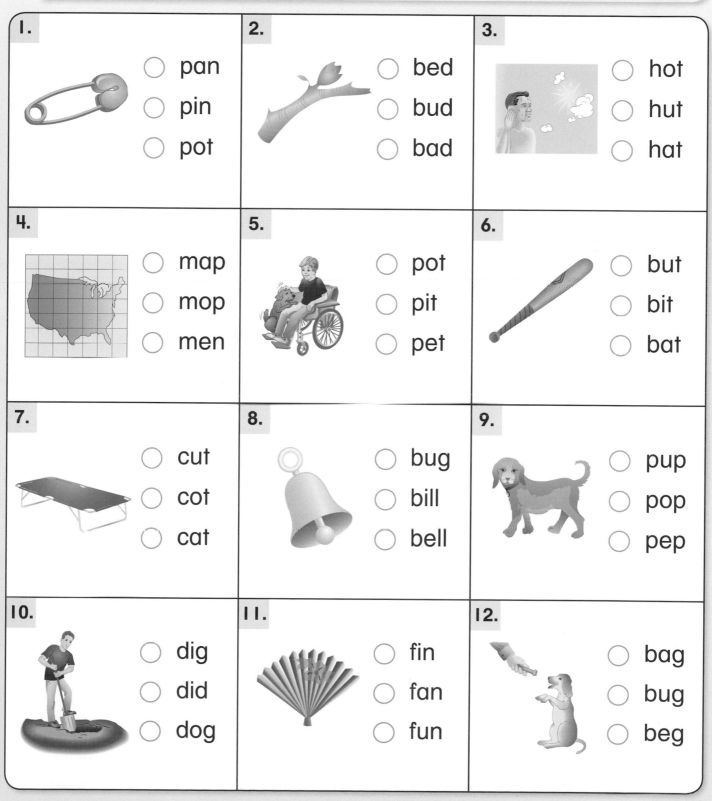

1.
- ○ pan
- ○ pin
- ○ pot

2.
- ○ bed
- ○ bud
- ○ bad

3.
- ○ hot
- ○ hut
- ○ hat

4.
- ○ map
- ○ mop
- ○ men

5.
- ○ pot
- ○ pit
- ○ pet

6.
- ○ but
- ○ bit
- ○ bat

7.
- ○ cut
- ○ cot
- ○ cat

8.
- ○ bug
- ○ bill
- ○ bell

9.
- ○ pup
- ○ pop
- ○ pep

10.
- ○ dig
- ○ did
- ○ dog

11.
- ○ fin
- ○ fan
- ○ fun

12.
- ○ bag
- ○ bug
- ○ beg

Check-Up **Say** the name of the picture. **Fill in** the circle next to the name of the picture.

1.	2.	3.
○ bag ○ dig ○ dog	○ hat ○ hot ○ hit	○ rug ○ rap ○ rip

4.	5.	6.
○ beg ○ bug ○ bit	○ pen ○ pin ○ pan	○ not ○ net ○ nut

7.	8.	9.
○ lips ○ laps ○ tops	○ cap ○ cob ○ cup	○ pat ○ pot ○ pet

10.	11.	12.
○ fog ○ bag ○ big	○ bid ○ bad ○ bed	○ mop ○ map ○ mud

13.	14.	15.
○ sit ○ wet ○ wag	○ fin ○ vet ○ van	○ pig ○ peg ○ pan

PHONICS ALIVE AT HOME Review this Check-Up with your child.

Name _____

Is It a Bug?

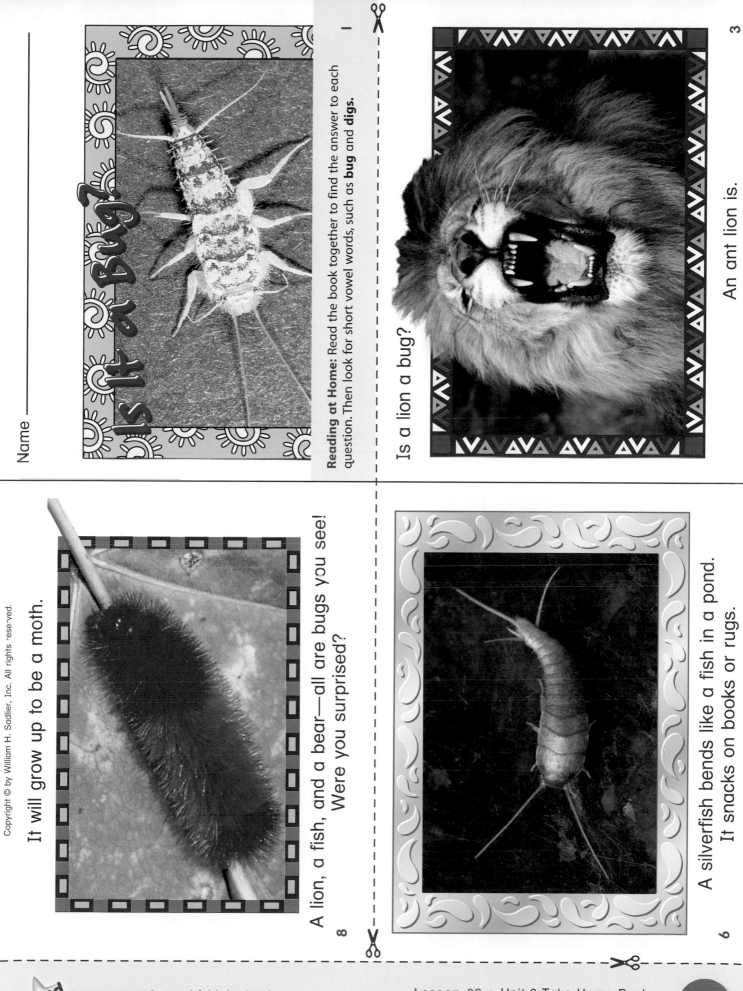

— 1

Reading at Home: Read the book together to find the answer to each question. Then look for short vowel words, such as **bug** and **digs.**

3

Is a lion a bug?

An ant lion is.

It will grow up to be a moth.

A lion, a fish, and a bear—all are bugs you see! Were you surprised?

8

A silverfish bends like a fish in a pond. It snacks on books or rugs.

6

DIRECTIONS: Cut and fold the book.

Lesson 89 • Unit 2 Take-Home Book
Comprehension: Setting a
Purpose for Reading

151

What is a bug?

I bet you'll be surprised.

4

An ant lion digs a pit to make a trap. It gobbles up other bugs that drop in.

Is a bear a bug?

A woolly bear is.

Is a fish a bug?

7

A silverfish is.

5

Yesterday's Paper

Yesterday's paper makes a hat,
Or a boat,
Or a plane,
Or a playhouse mat.

Yesterday's paper makes things
Like that—
And a very fine tent
For a sleeping cat.

Mabel Watts

Oral Language What else could you make out of old newspapers?
How might you recycle other things?

PHONICS ALIVE AT HOME

Name _____

Dear Family,

As your child learns about our environment in this unit, he or she will also be learning the sounds of the long and **r-**controlled vowels. You can participate by trying these activities together at home.

- Look at the pictures below. Say each letter and picture name with your child. Listen for the long vowel sounds.

Apreciada Familia:

Mientras aprenden sobre el medio ambiente los niños también aprenderán el sonido largo de las vocales. Pueden participar de estas actividades en el hogar.

- Miren los siguientes cuadros. Pronuncien cada letra y el nombre del objeto. Escuchen el sonido largo de las vocales.

a	i	o	u	e
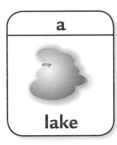	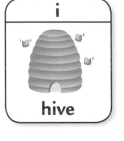			
lake	**hive**	**boat**	**mule**	**tree**

- Read the poem "Yesterday's Paper" on the reverse side of this page.

- Help your child find long vowel words in the poem, such as **makes, boat, plane, playhouse, like, fine,** and **sleeping.** Also find words with **r-**controlled vowels, such as **or, for,** and **paper.**

- Lean el poema "Yesterday's Paper" en la página 153.

- Ayuden al niño a encontrar vocales de sonido fuerte en el poema, como: **makes, boat, plane, playhouse, like, fine** y **sleeping.** También encuentren palabras con vocales y la letra **r,** como **or, for,** y **paper.**

PROJECT | PROYECTO

Recycle an old shoe box and some used magazines or catalogs. Help your child cut out pictures of things that have long vowel sounds or **r-**controlled vowels sounds. Put the pictures in the box. Ask your child to sort them according to the different vowel sounds.

Reciclen una caja de zapatos. Pida al niño recortar de revistas fotos de cosas que tengan vocales de sonido largo en sus nombres. Pongan las fotos en la caja. El niño puede ordenarlas de acuerdo a los diferentes sonidos.

 Visit us at **www.sadlierphonicsonline.com**

Work Together

Say the name of each picture. In each row, **circle** two pictures that have rhyming names. Make a new rhyming word and **print** it on the line. **Say** the rhyming words with a partner.

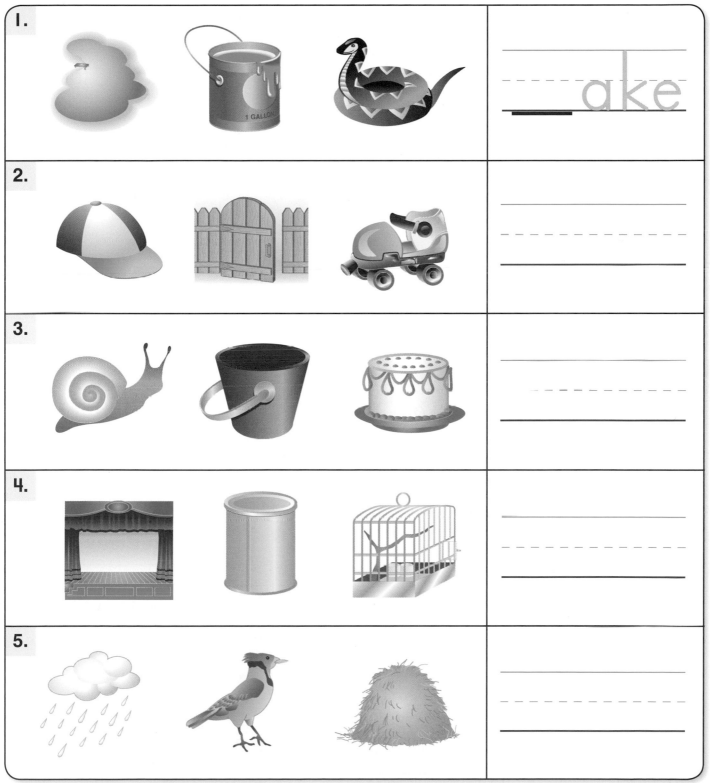

1. _____ ake

2.

3.

4.

5.

Say the name of the picture. **Color** each box that has a rhyming word.

1.

| day | say |
| game | hay |

jay

2.

| mail | vase |
| pail | tail |

sail

3.

| tape | cake |
| bake | take |

lake

4.

| wave | gave |
| save | nail |

cave

5.

| snail | skate |
| date | late |

gate

6.

| train | brain |
| safe | gain |

rain

7.

| cage | cape |
| age | page |

stage

8.

| tame | same |
| came | vase |

game

PHONICS ALIVE AT HOME Help your child cut apart the word squares. Then mix them up and match the rhyming words.

Say the word part. **Say** the name of the picture. **Print** the word on the line. **Add** your own rhyming word and picture.

_ ay	_ ake	_ ail
1.	4.	7.
2.	5.	8.
3.	6.	9.

Say the name of the picture. **Circle** its name.

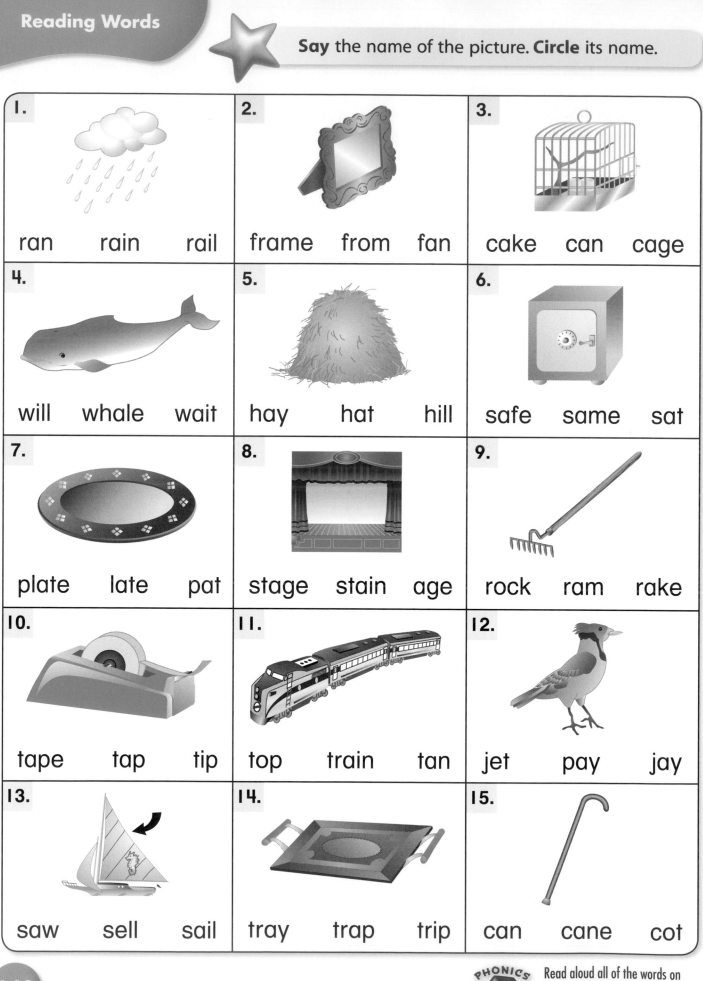

1. ran rain rail	**2.** frame from fan	**3.** cake can cage
4. will whale wait	**5.** hay hat hill	**6.** safe same sat
7. plate late pat	**8.** stage stain age	**9.** rock ram rake
10. tape tap tip	**11.** top train tan	**12.** jet pay jay
13. saw sell sail	**14.** tray trap trip	**15.** can cane cot

PHONICS ALIVE AT HOME Read aloud all of the words on the page. Have your child shout "Hooray!" after each long **a** word.

Work Together

Say the name of the picture with a partner. **Circle** its name and **print** it on the line.

1. lamp lake late	2. take tell tail	3. wait well wave
4. sell sail same	5. jay jet jam	6. game gum gate
7. name nail net	8. vane van vase	9. man make mail

Write a sentence about one picture. Use a long **a** word.

Lesson 95 • Writing Long Vowel **a**   **163**

Read the name of the picture. **Circle L** if its name has the sound of long **a**. **Circle S** if its name has the sound of short **a**.

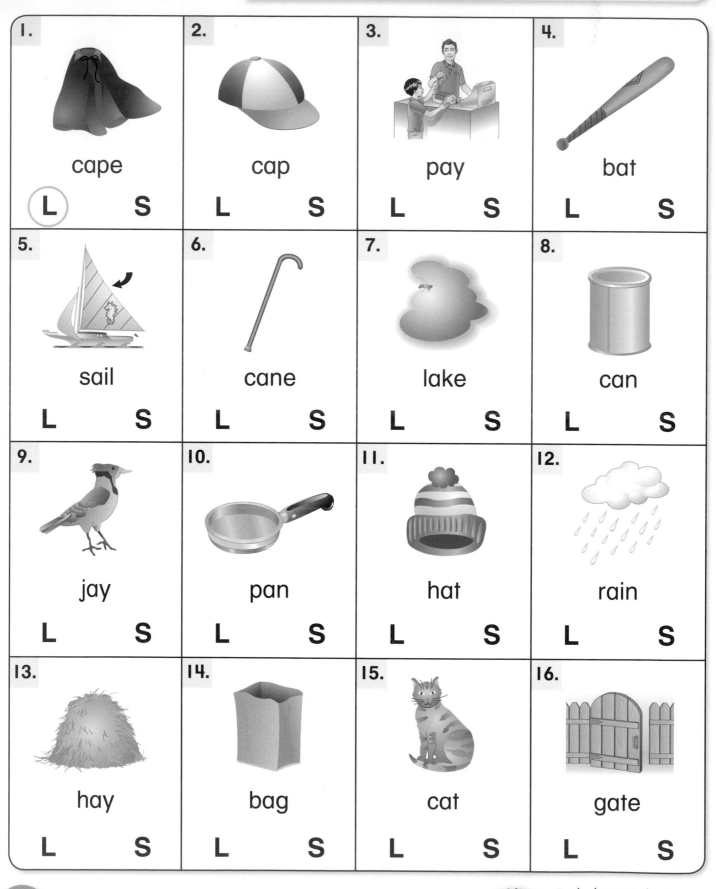

1.

cape

Ⓛ   S

2.

cap

L   S

3.

pay

L   S

4.

bat

L   S

5.

sail

L   S

6.

cane

L   S

7.

lake

L   S

8.

can

L   S

9.

jay

L   S

10.

pan

L   S

11.

hat

L   S

12.

rain

L   S

13.

hay

L   S

14.

bag

L   S

15.

cat

L   S

16.

gate

L   S

PHONICS ALIVE AT HOME   Randomly point to the pictures. Have your child wave for long **a** words and tap for short **a** words.

Ask your child to read this book to you. Then have him or her point out the long **a** words in the story.

Name _____

Game Day Box

Can you make up a game? Please come play with us.

8

Look at this big box. It will be our game day box.

1

We can sail far, far away. What can we play next?

6

We can play in this cave. What can we play next?

3

DIRECTIONS: Cut and fold the book. Read the story. If you come to a word you don't know, sound it out by looking at each letter. How does the box look different for each game?

We can play lots of games.
2 What can we play first?

We can bake a cake.
What can we play next? 7

We can play with this safe.
4 What can we play next?

We can send out the mail.
What can we play next? 5

Look at the picture. **Circle** the word that completes the sentence.
Print it on the line.

1.

Don't _____ paper scraps.

win
wet
waste

2.

Get an old picture _____ .

frame
from
flat

3.

_____ scraps onto it.

Pass
Pat
Paste

4.

Draw your _____ .

face
fan
fin

5.

_____ it in the frame.

Tap
Tape
Tip

6.

Hang it in a good _____ .

place
pal
plate

Visit **www.sadlierphonicsonline.com**
for another long **a** activity.

Lesson 97 • Long Vowel **a** in Sentences

167

Read the poem. Use long **a** words from the poem to complete the sentences.

Recycle Today

How can you stop waste today?
Tate and Miss Jay have a good way.

They say, "Save your lunch trays.
Don't toss them away.

Use them when you work.
Use them when you play.

Or use them to make gifts
for your friend's birthday!"

1. How can you stop _____ today?

2. Save your lunch _____ .

3. Use them when you _____ .

4. Use a tray to _____ a gift.

PHONICS ALIVE AT HOME Help your child read labels on cans of food you have at home. Talk about any long **a** words you find.

Read the story. **Print** three long **a** words from the story and three more long **a** words that you know. Then **read** all the words you wrote.

At the Lake

It is a hot day.
Kate jumps in the lake!
Nate rides a big wave.
Gail and Jane fill up a pail.
I wade with Mom.

The day gets late.
Kate and Nate help Mom pack up.
I can not stay awake.

Story Words

1. _____

2. _____

3. _____

My Words

1. _____

2. _____

3. _____

Save! Save! Save!

Recycle Time

Paper Glass Metal

Gail is recycling old mail and other things she has saved. **Write** about what you see. Use some long **a** words. **Look** at the words in the box if you need help.

Gail	save	mail	vase	take
gate	wait	wave	way	make

PHONICS ALIVE AT HOME Have your child read the long **a** words in the box. Have him or her tell what letters make the long **a** sound in each word.

Play tic-tac-toe by drawing a line through three pictures that have names with the sound of long **a**. On the whale, **print** the letters that stand for the long **a** sound in each game.

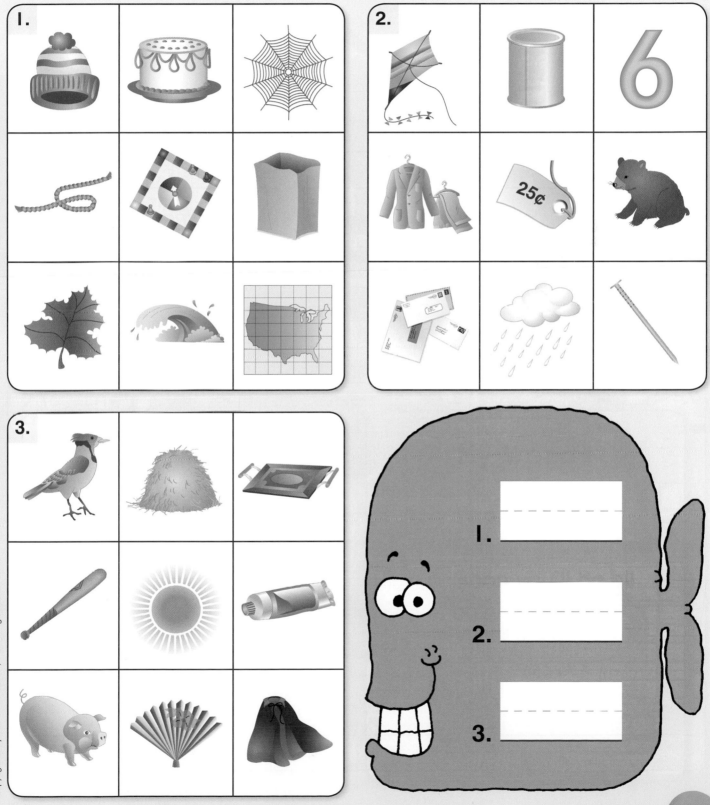

Check-Up

Say the name of the picture. If its name has the long **a** sound, **print** the letters to complete the word. Then **trace** the whole word.

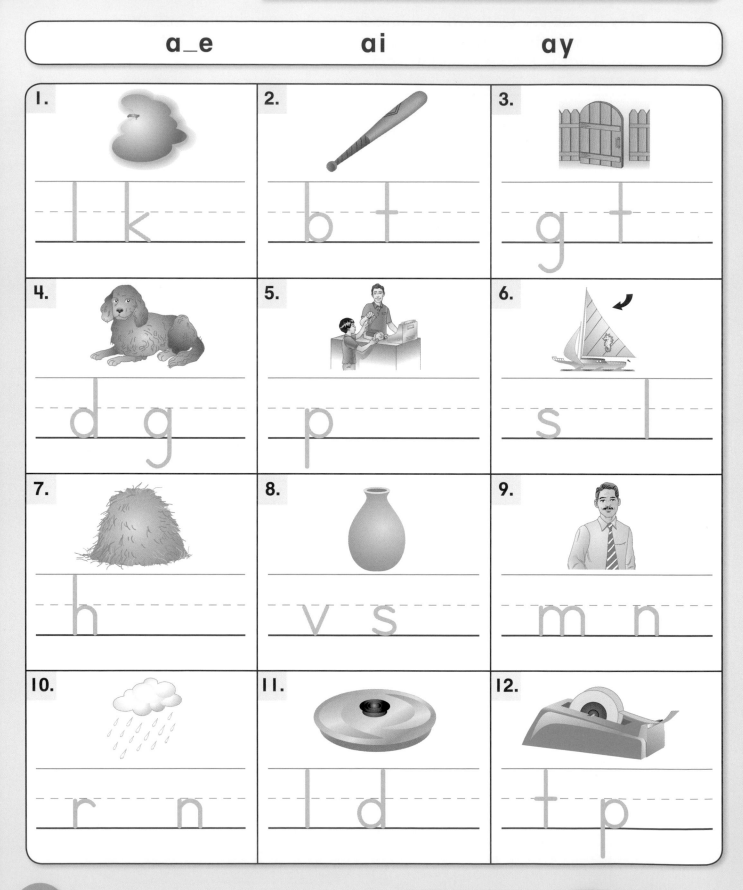

a_e	ai	ay

1. l___k

2. b___t

3. ___g___t

4. d___g

5. ___p___

6. s___l

7. h___

8. v___s___

9. m___n

10. r___n

11. l___d

12. t___p

 PHONICS ALIVE AT HOME Review this Check-Up with your child.

Listen

Listen as the page is read aloud. **Talk** about the long **i** words you hear, such as **five** and **vine**. **Circle** the hive.

Five in a Hive

Five bees wake up.
They leave the **hive.**
They see a **vine**
and down they dive.

I **like** bees.
They're very **wise**.
Bees do **fine** work
for their small **size**.

Oral Language What kind of work do bees do?

Hive has the long **i** sound. **Say** the name of the picture. **Circle** and **color** each picture that has the long **i** sound in its name.

1.
2.
3.
4.
5.
6.
7.
8.
9.
10.
11.
12.
13.
14.
15.
16.

PHONICS ALIVE AT HOME

Have your child say **hive** before each picture name (**hive/nine**) and tell if the vowel sounds are the same.

The letters **i_e** can stand for the long **i** sound. The letter **e** is silent. **Say** the name of the picture. **Print i** in the middle and **e** at the end of the word if it has the long **i** sound. Then **trace** the whole word.

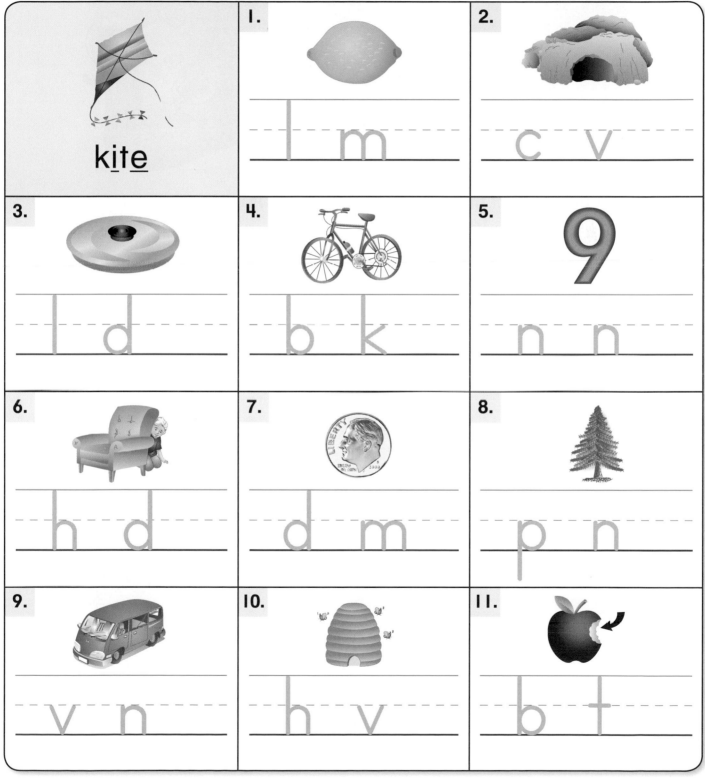

kite

1.

l m

2.

c v

3.

l d

4.

b k

5.

n n

6.

h d

7.

d m

8.

p n

9.

v n

10.

h v

11.

b t

The letters **igh** and **ie** can stand for the long **i** sound.

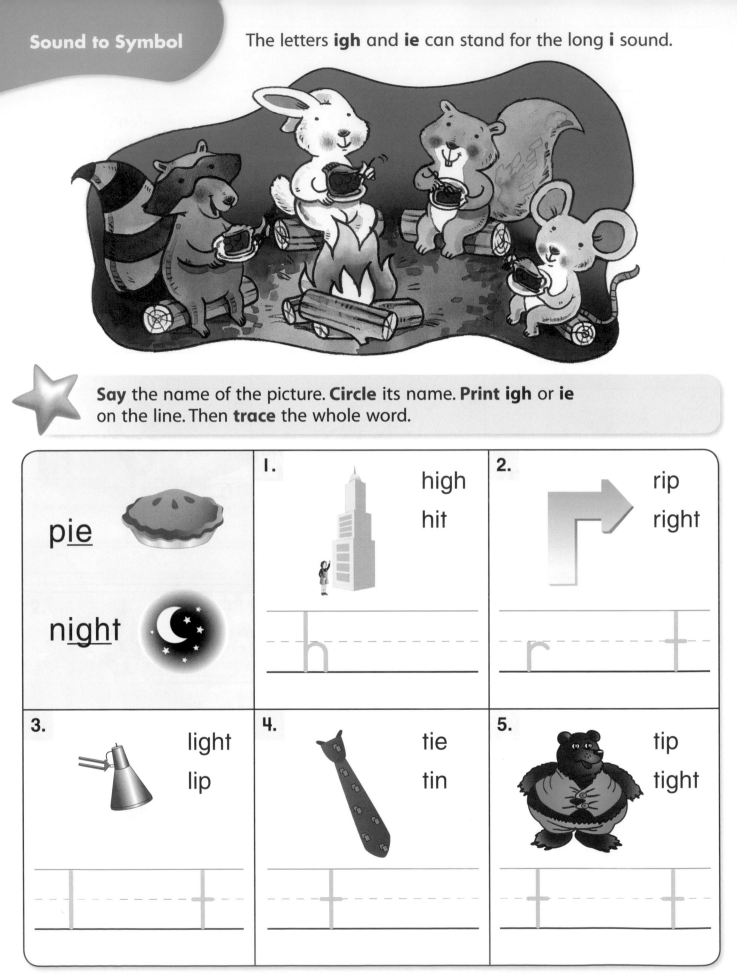

Say the name of the picture. **Circle** its name. **Print igh** or **ie** on the line. Then **trace** the whole word.

p<u>ie</u>

n<u>igh</u>t

1.
high
hit

h

2.
rip
right

r   t

3.
light
lip

t

4.
tie
tin

t

5.
tip
tight

t

PHONICS
ALIVE AT HOME

With your child, take turns naming the letters that stand for the long **i** sound in each word.

★ **Work Together**

Say the name of each picture. In each row, **circle** two pictures that have rhyming names. Make a new rhyming word. **Print** it on the line. **Say** the rhyming words with a partner.

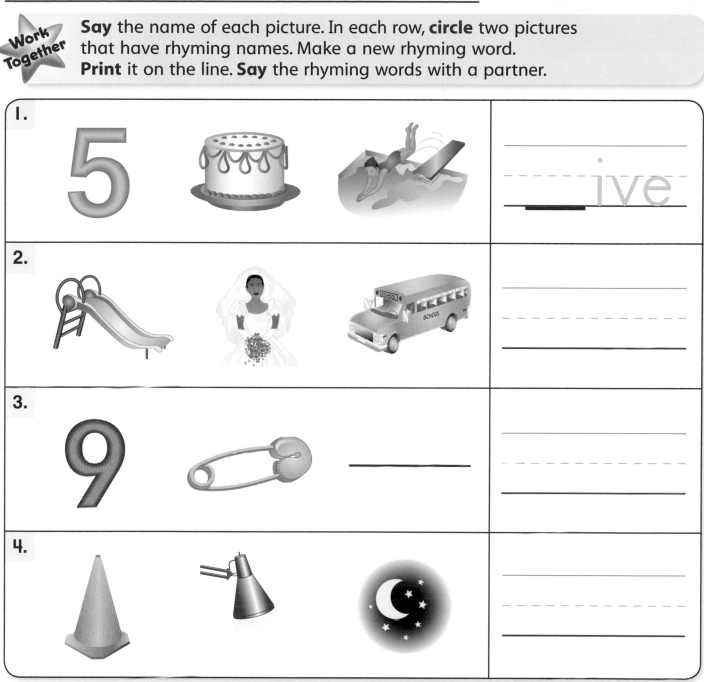

1. ___ive

2.

3. _____

4.

Add a letter in the hive to the word part below it. **Say** the new word. If the word is real, **print** it on the line.

h
f   d
p   n   v

_ine

w
s   k
h   r   t

_ide

r
p   t
m   l   n

_ight

1. fine
2.
3.
4.
5.

6.
7.
8.
9.
10.

11.
12.
13.
14.
15.

PHONICS ALIVE AT HOME With your child, build words by adding letters to _ime and _ile.

Say the name of the picture. **Circle** its name.

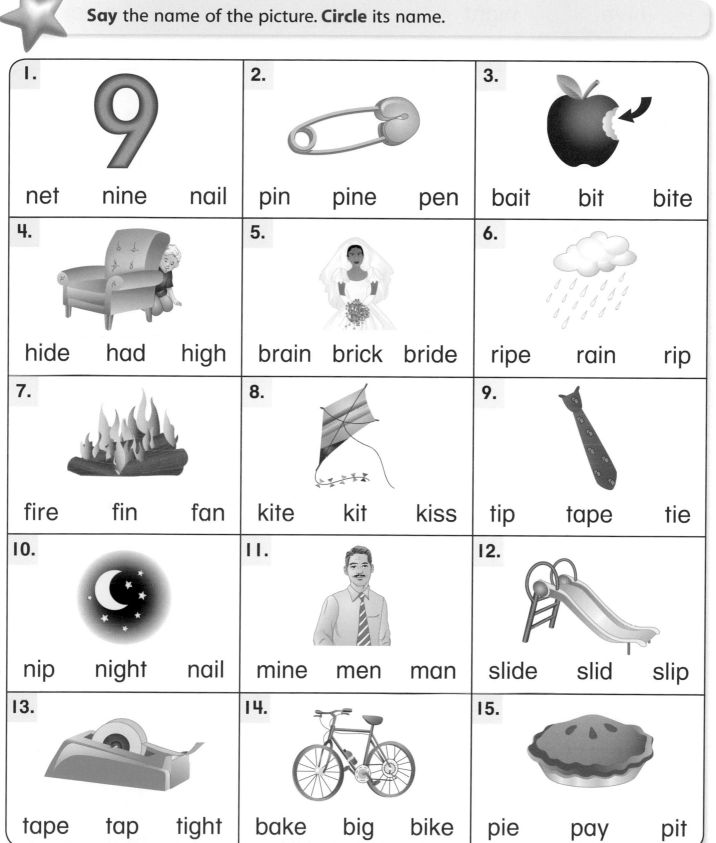

1. net nine nail	**2.** pin pine pen	**3.** bait bit bite
4. hide had high	**5.** brain brick bride	**6.** ripe rain rip
7. fire fin fan	**8.** kite kit kiss	**9.** tip tape tie
10. nip night nail	**11.** mine men man	**12.** slide slid slip
13. tape tap tight	**14.** bake big bike	**15.** pie pay pit

Writing Words

Use the picture clues and words in the box to **fill in** the puzzle. **Print** one letter in each box. **Write** a sentence about one picture. Use a long **i** word.

| hive | night | vine | tie | nine |

ACROSS ➡

1.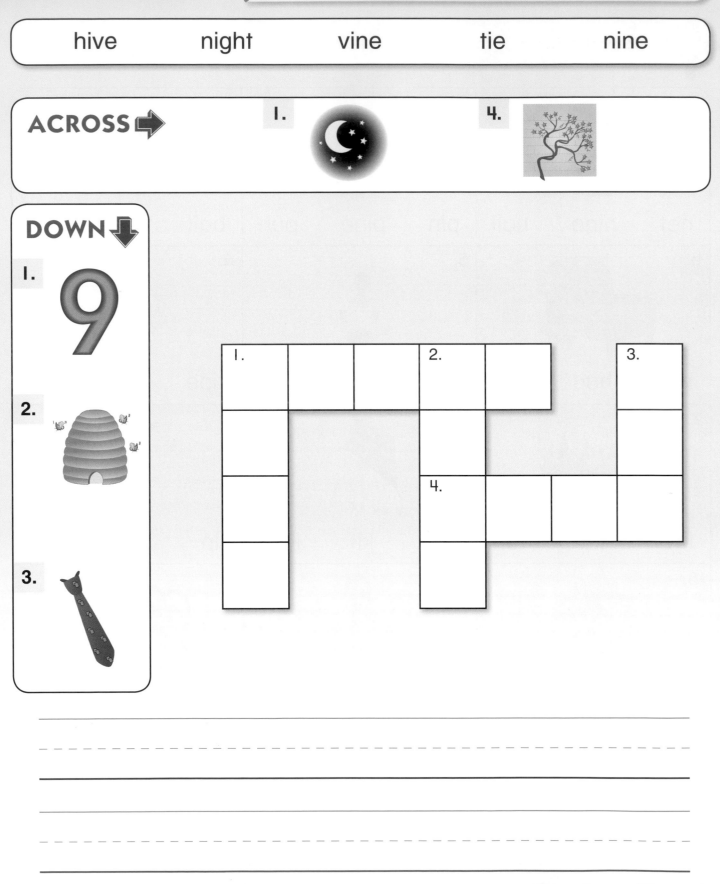

4.

DOWN ⬇

1. 9

2.

3.

PHONICS
ALIVE AT HOME
Have your child name each picture clue and point to the word in the puzzle.

Work Together **Say** the name of the picture. **Print** the word on the line.
Check your answers with a partner.

1.

2.

3.

4.

5.

6.

7.

8.

9.

10.

11.

12.

Say the name of each picture. **Print** the long **i** words in the Long **i** bin. **Print** the short **i** words in the Short **i** bin.

Long i

1. _____

2. _____

3. _____

4. _____

5. _____

Short i

6. _____

7. _____

8. _____

9. _____

10. _____

PHONICS ALIVE AT HOME Help your child turn these short **i** words into long **i** words: **bit, fin, rip, hid.** Have your child write the long **i** words you make.

Ask your child to read this book to you. Then have him or her point out the long **i** words in the story.

Read

Name _____

A Fine Sale

Yard Sale

Then Mike and Jen find Dad.
They let Dad make the pie!

8

It is a fine day. It is time for the yard sale.

1

Mike and Jen find a kite.
The tie makes a good tail.

6

Mike and Jen find a tire.
What else can they find?

3

DIRECTIONS: Cut and fold the book. Read the story. If you come to a word you don't know, sound it out by looking at each letter. Tell how Mike and Jen made each thing.

Lesson 105 • Long Vowel **i** Reader
Comprehension:
Drawing Conclusions

183

What a big pile! What will
2 Mike and Jen find?

The tire makes a good ride.
Ike likes to ride on the tire. 7

They find a tie and a mop.
4 What else can they find?

Jen finds a pie pan.
What else can they find? 5

Look at the picture. **Circle** the word that completes the sentence.
Print it on the line.

#			Words
1.		It is a _____ day.	fine fin fail
2.		We _____ to Pine Lake.	ride red rake
3.		It is on the _____ .	rate rig right
4.		We _____ and swim.	high hike him
5.		The _____ goes out.	fan fill fire
6.		It is _____ to go.	tail tie time

Visit **www.sadlierphonicsonline.com**
for another long **i** activity.

Read the poem. Use long **i** words from the poem to complete the sentences.

I Like the Earth

Day and night,
I like the earth.
I like tall pines
and buds that grow
on leafy vines.
I like fine lakes
where I can dive,
and bees that buzz
inside a hive.

1. I _____ the earth.

2. Buds grow on leafy _____.

3. I can _____ into lakes.

4. Bees buzz inside a _____.

PHONICS
ALIVE AT HOME

Help your child draw a
line under all of the long **i**
words in the poem.

Read the story. **Print** three long **i** words from the story and three more long **i** words that you know. Then **read** all the words you wrote.

The Bike and the Kite

The sun is high.
It is a fine day.
I ride my bike and see Mike.

I wave to Mike.
Mike has a kite.
Mike will let me help with his kite!
Mike and I get the kite high, high up!

I like Mike and his kite!

Story Words

1._____

2._____

3._____

My Words

1._____

2._____

3._____

A Five-Mile Hike

The children are on a hike. **Write** about what you see. Use some long **i** words. **Look** at the words in the box if you need help.

hike	might	time	vine	pine
five	hive	pile	mile	tie

PHONICS ALIVE AT HOME

Have your child read the long **i** words in the box. Talk about the letters that stand for the long **i** sound. Ask your child to spell each word.

Check-Up **Say** the name of the picture. If its name has the long **i** sound, **print** the letters to complete the word. Then **trace** the whole word.

i_e	igh	ie

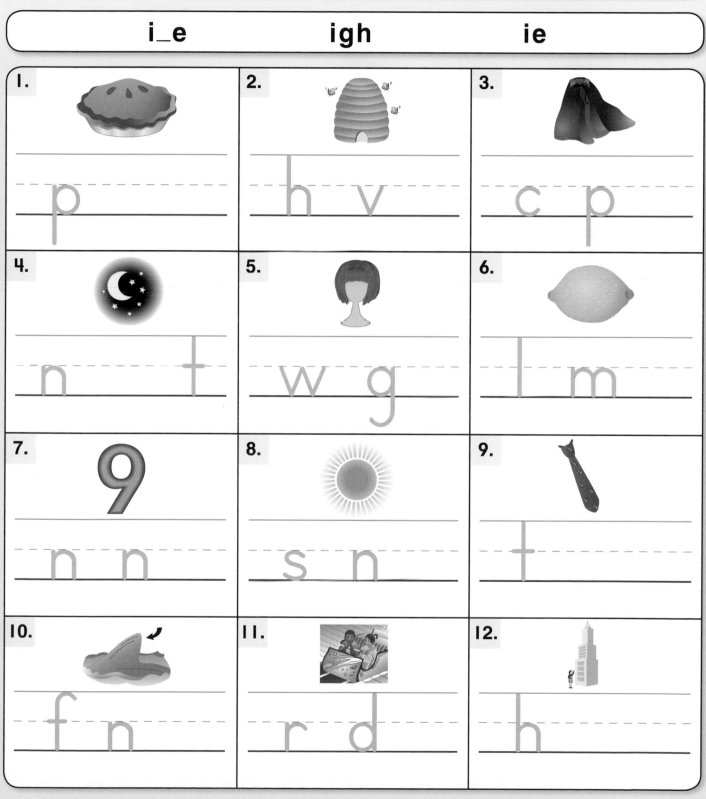

1. p___	2. h___v___	3. c___p___
4. n___t	5. w___g___	6. l___m___
7. n___n___	8. s___n	9. t___
10. f___n	11. r___d	12. h___

Print a or **i** in each empty box to make two words. **Read** the words across and down.

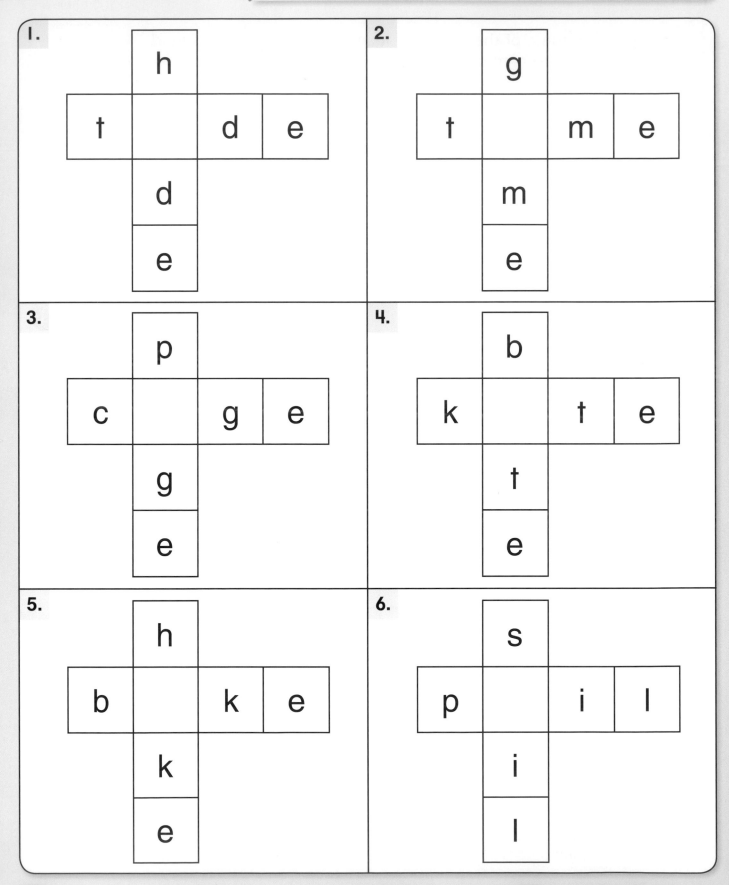

1.

h

t   d e

d

e

2.

g

t   m e

m

e

3.

p

c   g e

g

e

4.

b

k   t e

t

e

5.

h

b   k e

k

e

6.

s

p   i l

i

l

PHONICS
ALIVE AT HOME

Read the words in each puzzle. Ask your child to tell whether he or she hears long **a** or long **i**.

Listen as the page is read aloud. **Talk** about the long **o** words you hear, such as **snow** and **coat**. **Draw** a **nose**, **bow**, and **coat** on the snowman.

Listen

Let It Snow

I grab my **coat**
and out I **go**
to make a **snowman**
in the **snow**.

I'll **coast** down hills,
and make a fort.
A **snowy** day
is much too short!

Oral Language

What should you wear to play in the snow?

Rose has the long **o** sound. **Say** the name of the picture. **Circle** and **color** each picture that has the long **o** sound in its name.

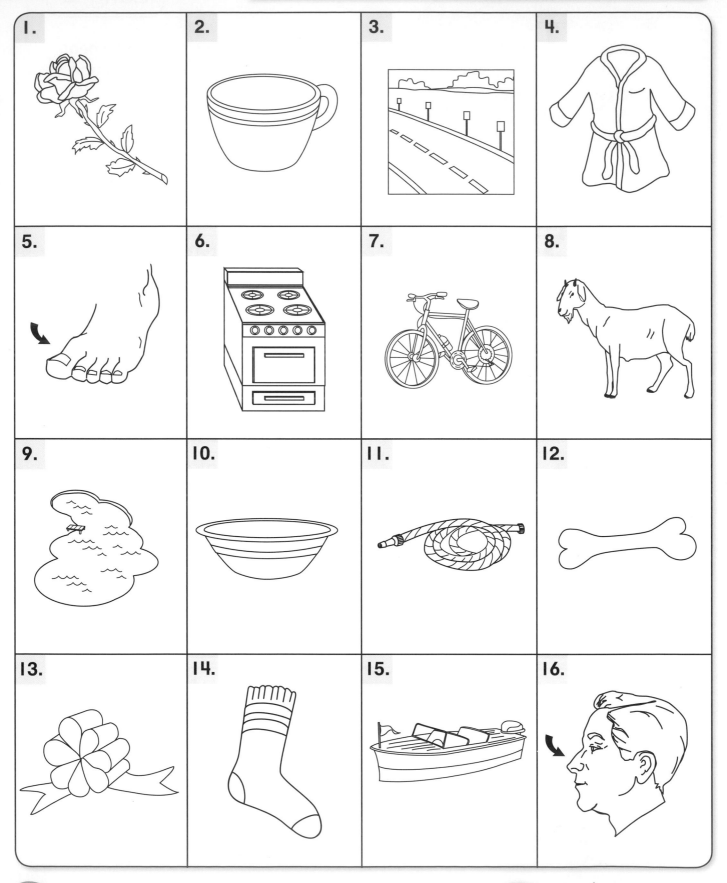

1.

2.

3.

4.

5.

6.

7.

8.

9.

10.

11.

12.

13.

14.

15.

16.

PHONICS ALIVE AT HOME

Name the pictures one at a time. Have your child point to his or her nose after every long **o** word.

The letters **o_e** can stand for the long **o** sound. The letter **e** is silent. **Say** the name of the picture. **Print o** in the middle and **e** at the end of the word if it has the long **o** sound. Then **trace** the whole word.

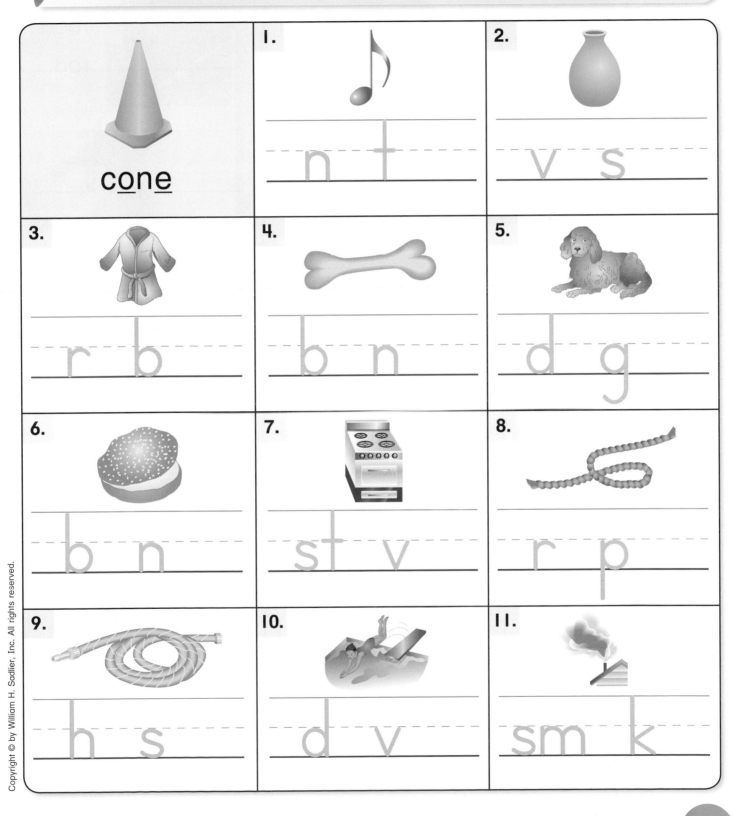

cone

1. n_t

2. v_s

3. r_b

4. b_n

5. d_g

6. b_n

7. st_v

8. r_p

9. h_s

10. d_v

11. sm_k

The letters **oa** and **ow** can stand for the long **o** sound. **Say** the name of the picture. **Circle** its name. **Print oa** or **ow** on the line. **Trace** the whole word.

b**oa**t

sn**ow**

1.
box
bow

b____

2.
road
rod

r____d

3.
row
rob

r____

4.
goat
got

g____t

5.
bop
bowl

b____l

6.
soap
sob

s____p

7.
mow
mop

m____

8.
cot
coat

c____t

PHONICS ALIVE AT HOME

Randomly read aloud the words on the page. Have your child stand on his or her tiptoes when he or she hears a long **o** word.

Say the name of the picture. **Color** each box that has a word that rhymes with the picture name.

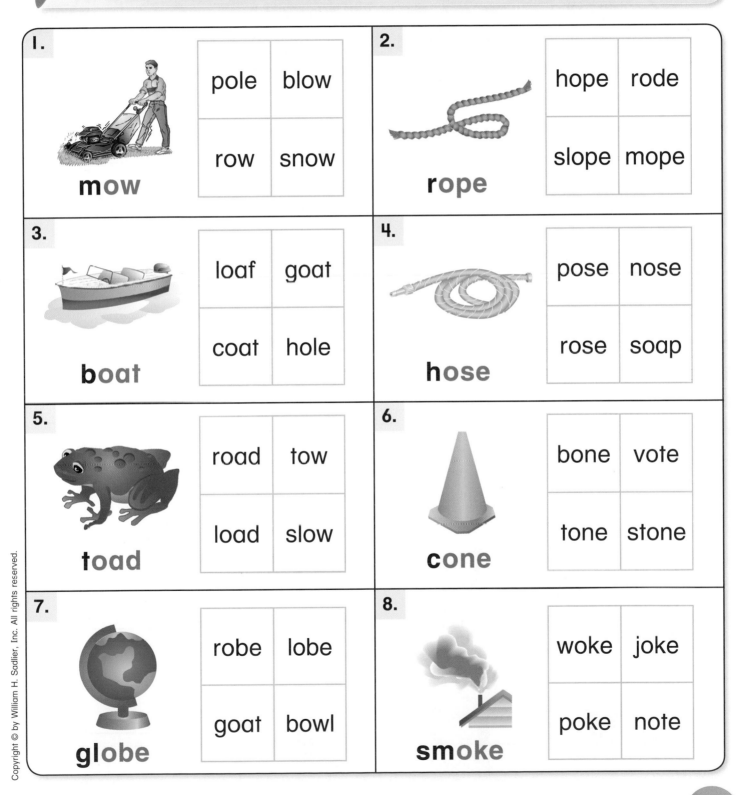

1.

pole	blow
row	snow

mow

2.

hope	rode
slope	mope

rope

3.

loaf	goat
coat	hole

boat

4.

pose	nose
rose	soap

hose

5.

road	tow
load	slow

toad

6.

bone	vote
tone	stone

cone

7.

robe	lobe
goat	bowl

globe

8.

woke	joke
poke	note

smoke

Work Together

Say the name of each picture. In each row, **circle** two pictures that have rhyming names. Make a new rhyming word. **Print** it on the line. **Say** the rhyming words with a partner.

1.

_____ OW

2.

3.

4.

PHONICS ALIVE AT HOME

Help your child use the new rhyming words in sentences.

Work Together

Say the word part. **Say** the name of the picture. **Print** the word on the line. **Add** your own rhyming word and picture. Work with a partner to make up more rhyming words.

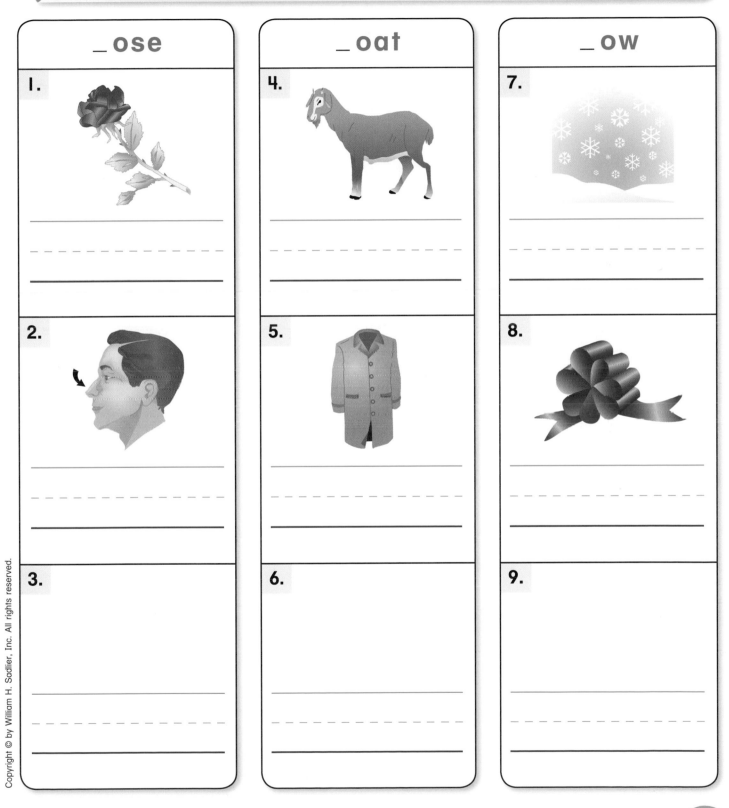

_ose	_oat	_ow
1.	4.	7.
2.	5.	8.
3.	6.	9.

Say the name of the picture. **Circle** its name.

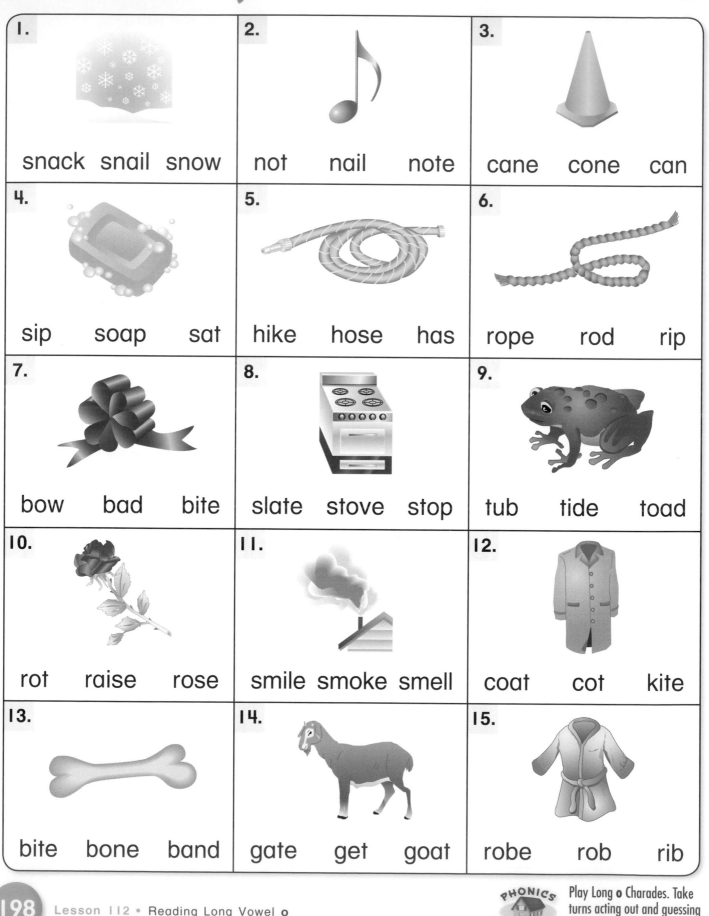

1. snack   snail   snow

2. not   nail   note

3. cane   cone   can

4. sip   soap   sat

5. hike   hose   has

6. rope   rod   rip

7. bow   bad   bite

8. slate   stove   stop

9. tub   tide   toad

10. rot   raise   rose

11. smile   smoke   smell

12. coat   cot   kite

13. bite   bone   band

14. gate   get   goat

15. robe   rob   rib

PHONICS ALIVE AT HOME   Play Long **o** Charades. Take turns acting out and guessing each picture's name.

Work Together **Say** the name of the picture with a partner. **Circle** its name and **print** it on the line.

1.	soap sip safe	2.	bake bite bone	3.	bun bat bowl

4.	ride road red	5.	note night not	6.	tie toe time

7.	hole hat hill	8.	net name nose	9.	rip rope ripe

Write a sentence about one picture. Use a long **o** word.

Visit **www.sadlierphonicsonline.com** for another long **o** activity.

Read the name of the picture. **Circle L** for the long **o** sound, or **S** for the short **o** sound. **Color** the pictures with the long **o** sound.

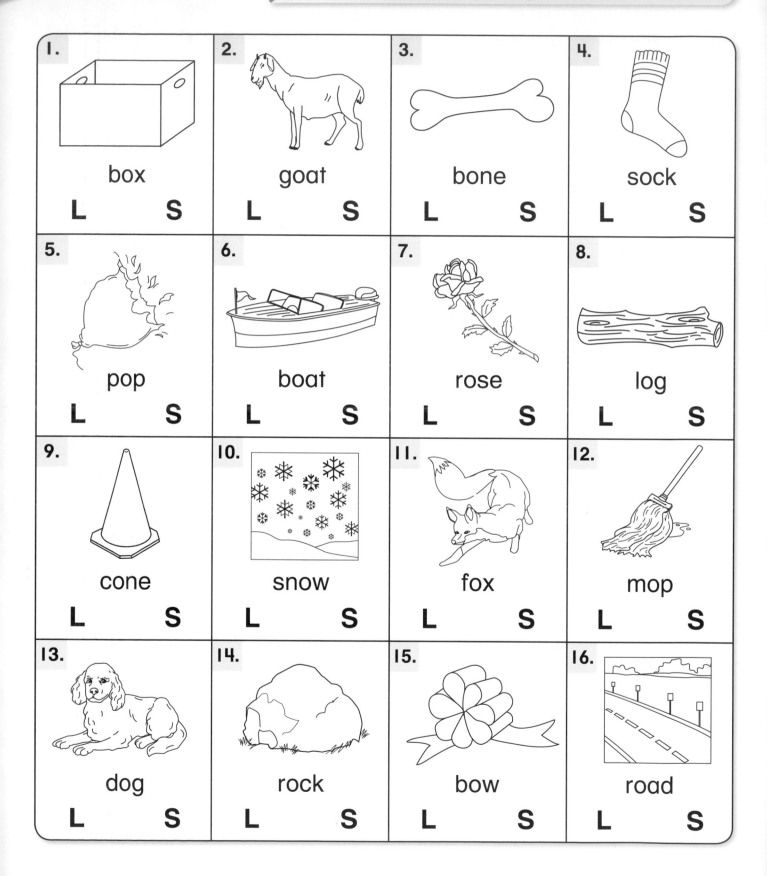

1. box
L   S

2. goat
L   S

3. bone
L   S

4. sock
L   S

5. pop
L   S

6. boat
L   S

7. rose
L   S

8. log
L   S

9. cone
L   S

10. snow
L   S

11. fox
L   S

12. mop
L   S

13. dog
L   S

14. rock
L   S

15. bow
L   S

16. road
L   S

PHONICS ALIVE AT HOME Have your child color the vowels in each word yellow. Point out that short **o** words usually have only one vowel.

Ask your child to read this book to you. Then have him or her point out the long **o** words in the story.

Read

Name _____

Joan and Toad

Fold

Toad and Joan have so
8 much fun. What a nice home!

Joan is in her boat.
She rows and rows.   1

Fold

Toad jumps into the lake.
6 He likes the lake.

Toad shows Joan his home.
His home is a mess!   3

DIRECTIONS: Cut and fold the book. Read the story. If you come to a word you don't know, sound it out by looking at each letter. Tell why Joan helped Toad.

Lesson 114 • Long Vowel **o** Reader
Comprehension: Understanding
Cause and Effect

201

Joan is going to see Toad.
Toad and Joan are friends.

2

Joan jumps into the lake.
She likes the lake, too.

7

Joan will help Toad.
They will fix Toad's home.

4

Joan uses a pole and a bag.
Look! No more mess!

5

Work Together Look at the picture. **Circle** the word that completes the sentence.
Print it on the line. Take turns reading the sentences with a partner.

1.	Look at the _____ .	snip snake snow
2.	It is _____ white at first.	so say sock
3.	There is dirt on the _____ .	rope rake road
4.	It is from _____ .	smile smoke smell
5.	Snow _____ up dirt.	soaps soaks sacks
6.	Our _____ do, too.	cots cast coats

Tadpole to Toad

My tadpole floats in its home.
Its home is a big bowl.
The bowl has stones,
pond water, plants, and mud.

Is my tadpole a fish? No!
It will grow to be a toad.
I hope it grows up soon!
Then I'll let it go.

1. My tadpole _____ in its home.

2. My tadpole lives in a _____ .

3. My tadpole will grow to be a _____ .

4. I hope it _____ up soon!

PHONICS
ALIVE AT HOME

Have your child find long **o**
words in the story with these
spellings: **o_e, oa, ow,** and **o.**

Read the story. **Print** three long **o** words from the story and three more long **o** words that you know. Then **read** all the words you wrote.

Rose Mows

Rose is a toad.
Rose has a big job.
Rose mows by the gate.
Rose mows by the road.
Rose mows by the pole.
Rose mows in the day.
Rose mows in the night.
Rose mows and mows.
Nice job, Rose!

Story Words

1. _____

2. _____

3. _____

My Words

1. _____

2. _____

3. _____

WELCOME TO CAMP LA-GOAT-TA

⭐ The goats are having fun at Camp La-Goat-Ta. **Write** about what you see. Use some long **o** words. **Look** at the words in the box if you need help.

goat	row	boat	note	home
rope	hope	rode	bow	toad

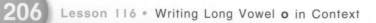

PHONICS
ALIVE AT HOME

Have your child read the long **o** words in the box. Ask him or her to spell each word and use it in a sentence.

Check-Up

Say the name of the picture. If its name has the long **o** sound, find the letters in the box to complete the word. **Print** the letters on the line. Then **trace** the whole word.

o_e	oa	ow

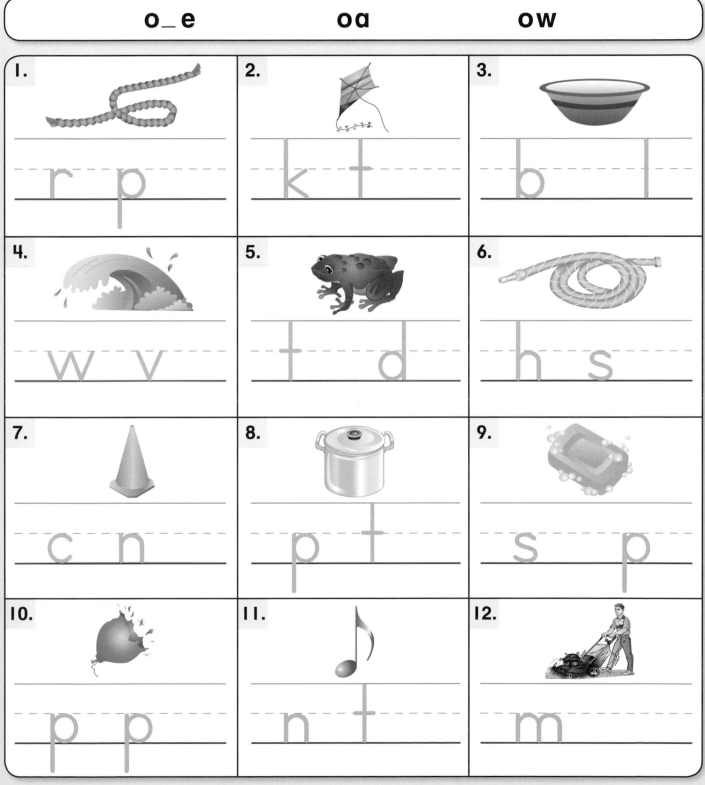

1.
r p

2.
k t

3.
b l

4.
w v

5.
t d

6.
h s

7.
c n

8.
p t

9.
s p

10.
p p

11.
n t

12.
m

Combine words from boxes 1, 2, and 3 to make sentences. **Print** them on the lines. **Underline** the long vowel words in your sentences.

1.	2.	3.
Kate and Jay	hike	to the lake.
Joan and Mike	race	down the road.
Five men	rode	at night.

Lesson 117 • Reviewing Long Vowels **a, i, o**

PHONICS ALIVE AT HOME

Help your child make up endings to these sentences: Mike likes to _____. Mrs. Dole bakes _____.

Check-Up **Say** the name of the picture. **Circle** its name and **print** it on the line.

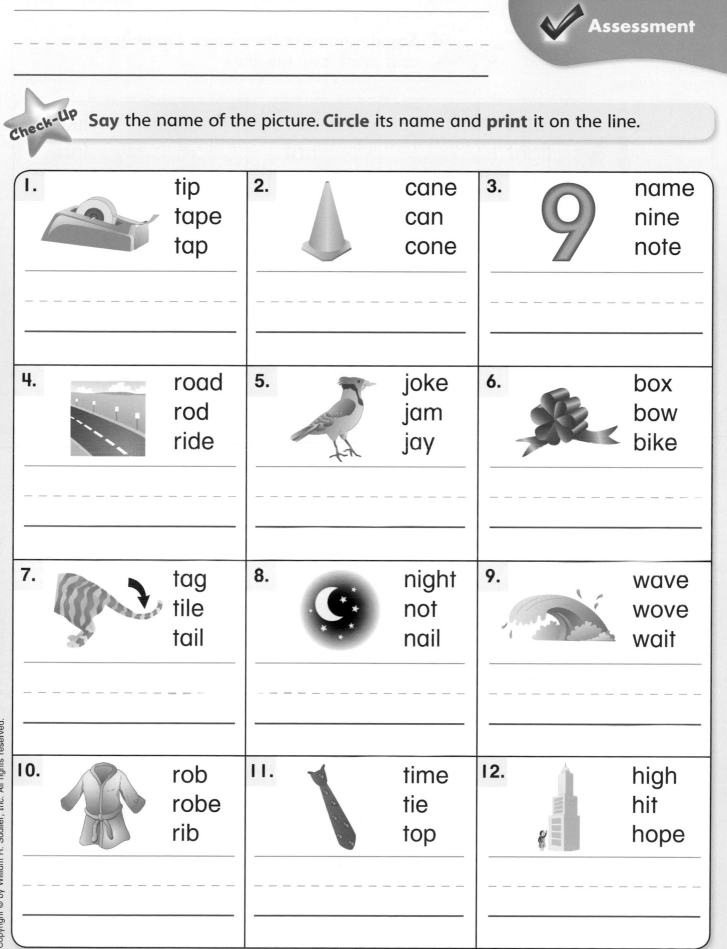

1.	tip tape tap	2.	cane can cone	3.	name nine note
4.	road rod ride	5.	joke jam jay	6.	box bow bike
7.	tag tile tail	8.	night not nail	9.	wave wove wait
10.	rob robe rib	11.	time tie top	12.	high hit hope

Visit **www.sadlierphonicsonline.com** for another activity with long **a**, long **i**, and long **o**.

Check-Up Say the name of the picture. **Circle** its name and **print** it on the line.

1.	load light late	2.	note not night	3.	like lab lake
4.	hose hole hive	5.	pail pie pole	6.	cap cope cape
7.	mole mail mile	8.	got gate goat	9.	line lime lane
10.	vane vine van	11.	high hay ham	12.	row road ray

PHONICS ALIVE AT HOME Review this Check-Up with your child.

Listen as the page is read aloud. **Talk** about the long **u** words you hear, such as **blue** and **fruit**. Then **tell** one thing you like about June.

June

Bright **blue** skies,
bathing **suits**,
inner **tubes**,
fresh, ripe **fruit**,
sandy **dunes**,
happy **tunes**,
barbecues—
I love **June**!

Oral Language How are people in the picture making the beach a safe and clean place?

June has the long **u** sound. **Say** the name of the picture. **Circle** and **color** each picture that has the long **u** sound in its name.

PHONICS ALIVE AT HOME

Help your child cut apart the pictures. Mix them up and take turns finding the ones with long **u** in their names.

The letters **u__e** can stand for the long **u** sound. The letter **e** is silent. **Say** the name of the picture. **Print u** in the middle and **e** at the end of the word if it has the long **u** sound. Then **trace** the whole word.

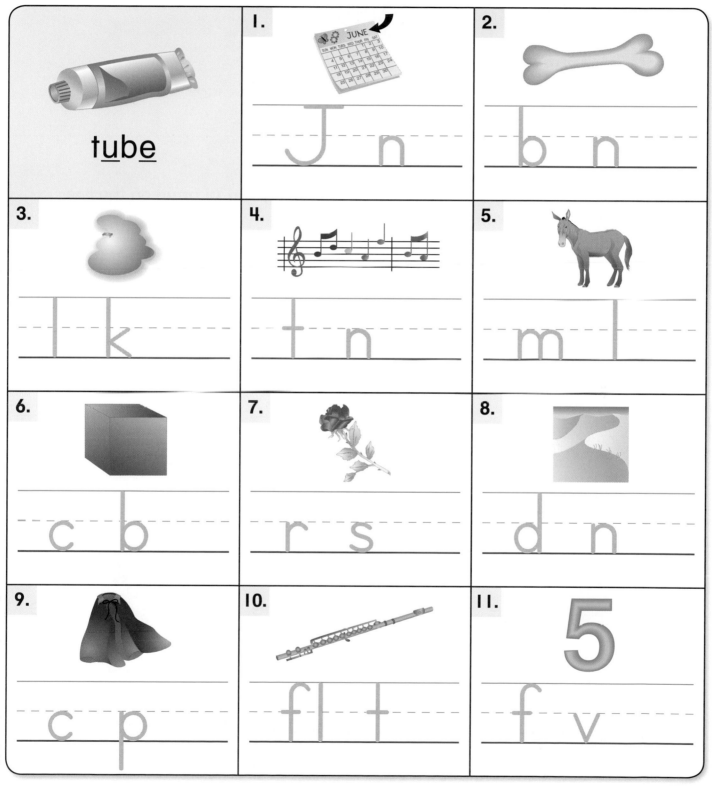

	1.	2.
t**u**b**e**	J __ n	b __ n
3.	**4.**	**5.**
l __ k	t __ n	m __ l
6.	**7.**	**8.**
c __ b	r __ s	d __ n
9.	**10.**	**11.**
c __ p	f l __ t	f __ v

The letters **ui** and **ue** can stand for the long **u** sound.

Say the name of the picture. **Circle** its name. **Print ui** or **ue** on the line. Then **trace** the whole word.

---

fr<u>ui</u>t

bl<u>ue</u>

1.
suit
sun

s____t

2.
gum
glue

gl____

3.
fruit
fume

fr____t

4.
juice
June

j____ce

5.
sub
Sue

S____

First have your child point to and read all of the words with **ui**. Then have him or her do the same for the **ue** words.

⭐ **Draw** a line through three boxes in a row with words or pictures that have the long **u** sound. **Print** the letters that stand for the long **u** sound on the cube.

1.

(toothpaste)	soap	hive
tune	June	(bathtub)
mule	(bell)	gate

2.

juice	suit	(fruit)
(cake)	blue	pine
vine	(cup)	paint

3.

(net)	hut	dune
glue	(paint blob)	clue
lime	boat	(dog)

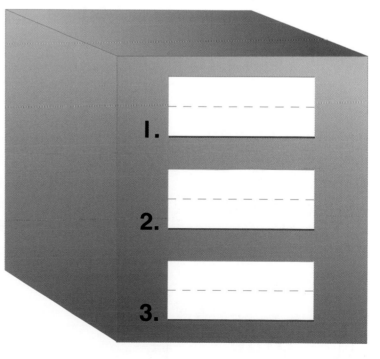

1.

2.

3.

In each row, **circle** the word that rhymes with the name of the picture.

1. flute	(cute)	cut	cane
2. cube	tape	tub	tube
3. dune	tone	tune	time
4. fruit	suit	size	sun
5. mule	rail	rule	run
6. glue	plum	cub	blue

PHONICS ALIVE AT HOME

Have your child choose two rhyming words. Work together to use them in a short, silly poem.

Work Together Say the word part. Say the name of the picture. Print the word on the line. Work with a partner to add your own rhyming words.

1. _ une

2. _ uit

3. _ ube

4. _ ue

5. _ ute

Say the name of the picture. **Circle** its name.

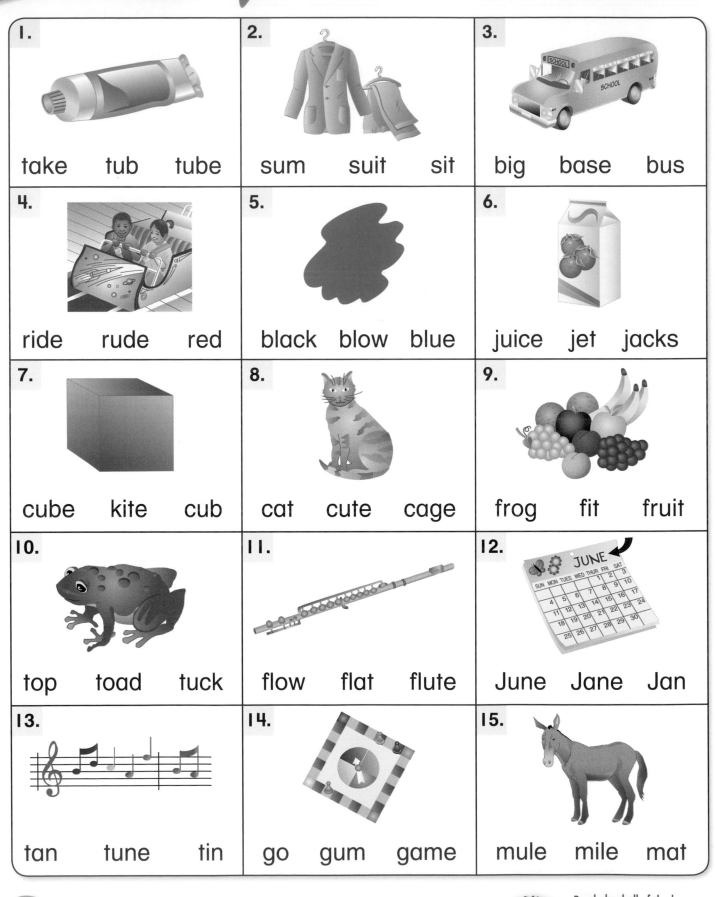

1. take tub tube	2. sum suit sit	3. big base bus
4. ride rude red	5. black blow blue	6. juice jet jacks
7. cube kite cub	8. cat cute cage	9. frog fit fruit
10. top toad tuck	11. flow flat flute	12. June Jane Jan
13. tan tune tin	14. go gum game	15. mule mile mat

Read aloud all of the long **u** words on the page. Have your child spell each word to you.

Say the name of the picture. **Circle** its name and **print** it on the line.

1.	mile mule mail	2.	tame tab tune	3.	cube code cut
4.	black bud blue	5.	fruit fat fun	6.	tape tube time
7.	sit sun suit	8.	just juice jam	9.	date dime dune

Write a sentence about one picture. Use a long **u** word.

Say the name of each picture. **Print** the long **u** words under the Long **u** tube. **Print** the short **u** words under the Short **u** tube.

Long u

Short u

1. _____

2. _____

3. _____

4. _____

5. _____

6. _____

PHONICS ALIVE AT HOME

Print **tub**, **cut**, and **cub**. Have your child add **e** to the end of each word to make a new word.

DUKE

Ask your child to read this book to you. Then have him or her point out the long **u** words in the story.

Read

Name _____

A Pet Mule

Fold

8 Sue helped Duke. Now Sue and Duke are best friends.

It was the start of June. Sue got a new pet mule. 1

Do not run and be rude!

Fold

6 She read Duke the first rule: "Do not run and be rude!"

Sue made Duke a cute suit. She took Duke for a walk. 3

DIRECTIONS: Cut and fold the book. Read the story. If you come to a word you don't know, sound it out by looking at each letter. Could this story really happen?

Sue named her pet mule Duke. She put his name on his house.

2

Duke learned the rules. Duke helped Sue.

7

Duke was rude. He ran away and made a mess.

4

Duke must learn some rules. Sue came home and made a sign.

5

Work Together Look at the picture. **Circle** the word that completes the sentence. **Print** it on the line. **Explain** to a partner how to make a cardboard flute.

1. Sue will make a _____ .

fun
flute
flat

2. She will use a _____ .

tub
tape
tube

3. She will paint it _____ .

blow
blue
bug

4. Luke will bring his _____ .

tuba
tag
tug

5. June will _____ an old box.

use
us
as

6. They will play a _____ .

toad
tan
tune

 Visit **www.sadlierphonicsonline.com** for another long **u** activity.

Read the riddle. Use long **u** words to complete the sentences.

What Am I?

I have blue skies,
huge seas,
lively beasts,
ripe fruit,
soft winds that sound
like flutes,
and beauty everywhere.

Rude people pollute me.
My true friends salute me.
What am I?

_____

1. Earth's friends like _____ skies.

_____

2. Earth's friends like ripe _____ .

_____

3. Earth's friends do not _____ .

_____

4. Earth's _____ friends salute it.

224 Lesson 125 • Long Vowel **u** in Context
Comprehension: Recalling Details

Ask your child to read aloud the clues that helped him or her answer the riddle.

Read the story. **Print** three long **u** words from the story and three more long **u** words that you know. Then **read** all the words you wrote.

June and I

June and I like blue.
June has a blue bow
and a cute blue suit.
I have a blue bike
and a fine blue kite.
June has a big blue tube.
It has blue glue in it.
I have a big blue cup.
It has blue juice in it.

June and I like blue—do you?

Story Words

1. _____
2. _____
3. _____

My Words

1. _____
2. _____
3. _____

A Day in June

June

It's breakfast time before school. **Write** about what you see. Use some long **u** words. **Look** at the words in the box if you need help.

tune	flute	glue	blue	June
fruit	juice	cute	Sue	suit

PHONICS ALIVE AT HOME Ask your child to write the long **u** words from the box and then sort the words by their long **u** spelling.

Check-Up

Say the name of the picture. If its name has the long **u** sound, find the letters in the box to complete the word. **Print** the letters on the line. Then **trace** the whole word.

u _ e	ui	ue

1.

t ___ n

2.

g l ___

3.

j ___ g

4.

c ___ b

5.

r ___ w

6.

s ___ t

7.

b l ___

8.

d ___ n

9.

l ___ t

10.

c ___ p

11.

f r ___ t

12.

m ___ l

Reorder the words to make a sentence. **Print** the sentence on the line. **Circle** the long vowel words in your sentence.

I. blue. bike is The

The (bike) is (blue).

2. June. in nice is It

3. on logs. Toads play

4. There snow. no is

5. coats away. our We put

6. ride We bikes day. all

PHONICS ALIVE AT HOME

Have your child read the sentences to you. Then take turns finding the long **a, i, o,** and **u** words.

Listen as the page is read aloud. **Talk** about the long **e** words you hear, such as **green** and **trees**. Complete the picture by drawing a person or animal.

Green Trees

Green trees,
green trees!
They give us wood
and things to **eat**.
Branches hold
our swing's fine **seat**.
We think **trees**
are really **neat**.

Oral Language What things made from trees do you see in your classroom?

Say the name of the pictures in each row. **Circle** the pictures with names that have the long **e** sound.

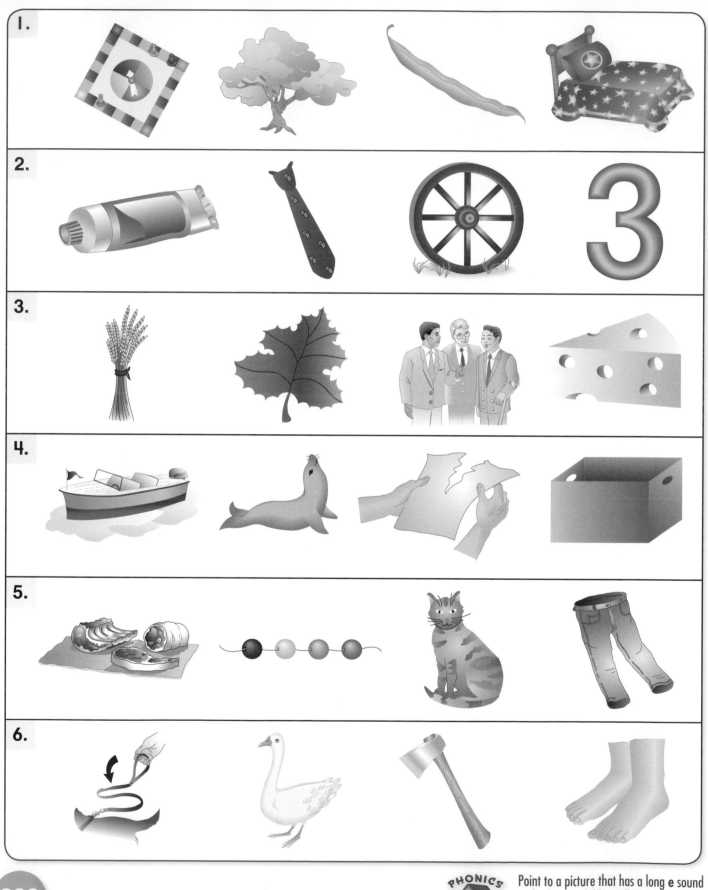

1.

2.

3.

4.

5.

6.

230 Lesson 128 • Phonemic Awareness: /ē/

PHONICS ALIVE AT HOME

Point to a picture that has a long **e** sound and ask your child to tell you a word that rhymes with the picture name.

The letters **ea** can stand for the long **e** sound. **Say** the name of the picture. **Print ea** in the middle of the word if it has the long **e** sound. Then **trace** the whole word.

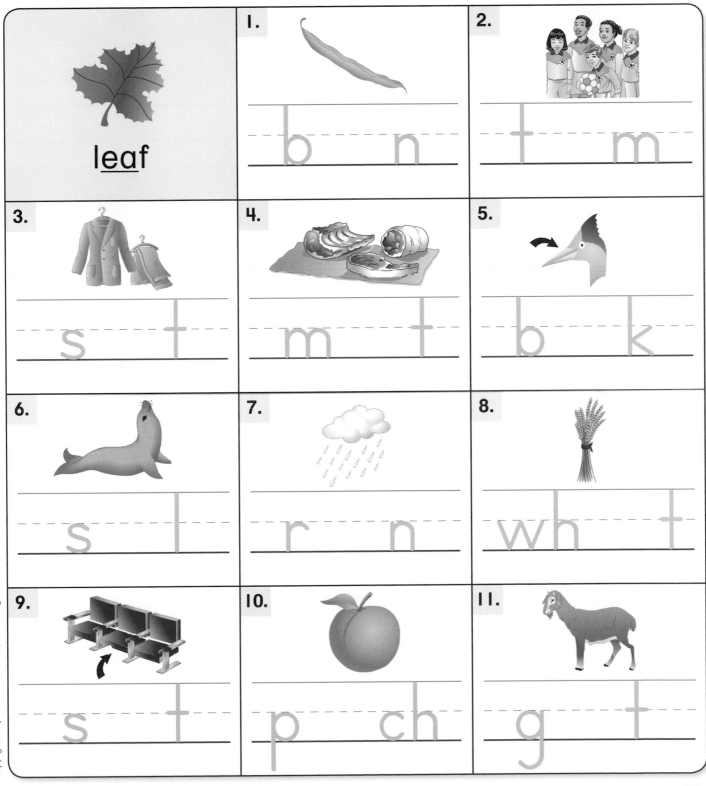

	1.	2.
leaf	b___n	t___m
3.	4.	5.
s___t	m___t	b___k
6.	7.	8.
s___l	r___n	wh___t
9.	10.	11.
s___t	p___ch	g___t

The letters **ee** can stand for the long **e** sound. **Say** the name of the picture. **Print ee** if it has the long **e** sound. Then **trace** the whole word.

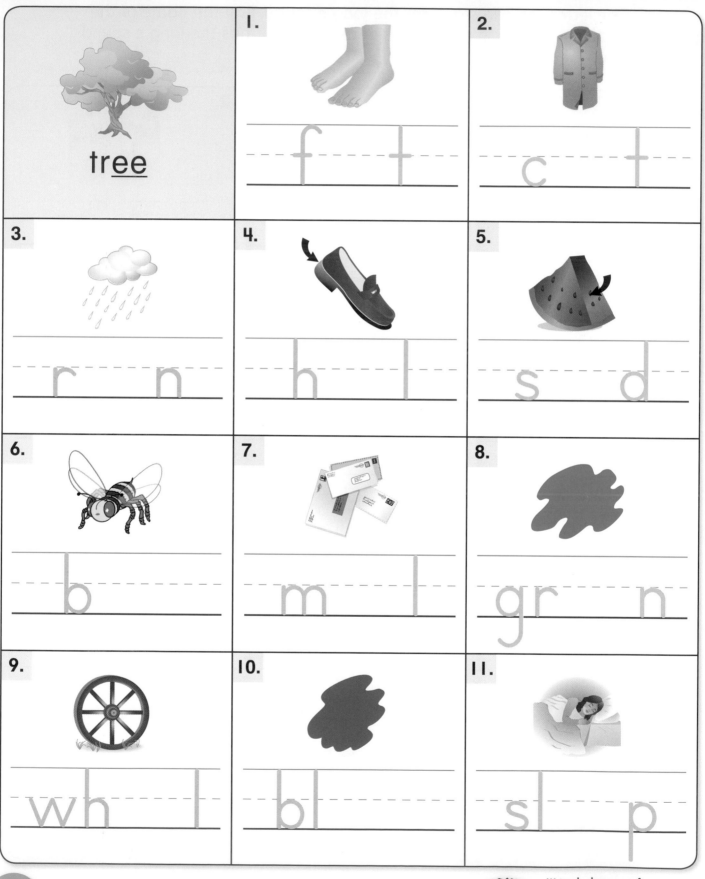

tree

1. f ___ t

2. c ___ t

3. r ___ n

4. h ___ l

5. s ___ d

6. b ___

7. m ___ l

8. gr ___ n

9. wh ___ l

10. bl ___

11. sl ___ p

PHONICS ALIVE AT HOME Write the letters **ee** five times on a sheet of paper. Have your child add letters to make long e words.

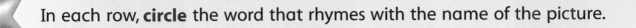

In each row, **circle** the word that rhymes with the name of the picture.

1. team	steam	step	tent
2. read	rid	bead	bid
3. queen	grin	green	quite
4. seat	set	met	meat
5. heel	peel	pet	help
6. beak	beg	lick	leak

⭐ **Say** the word part. **Say** the name of the picture. **Print** the word on the line. **Add** your own rhyming word and picture.

_ee

1.

2.

3.

_eel

4.

5.

6.

_eat

7.

8.

9.

PHONICS ALIVE AT HOME

Read one of the words on the page. Have your child name words that rhyme with the word you read.

Add the letter or letters on the petal to the word part below it.
Say the new word. **Print** it on the line.

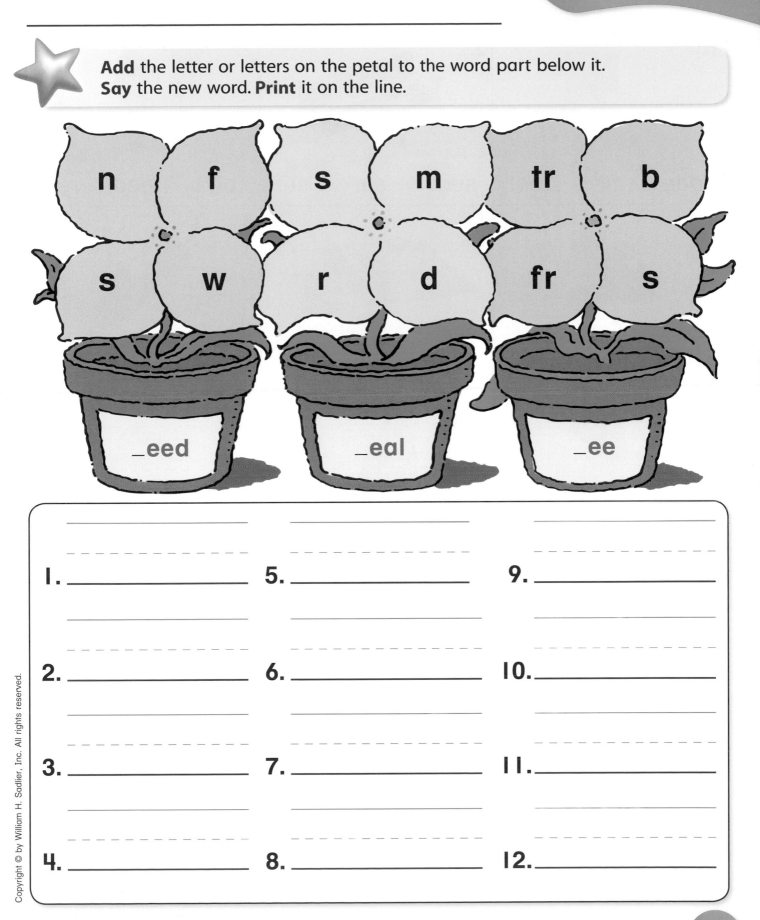

n   f   s   m   tr   b

s   w   r   d   fr   s

_eed   _eal   _ee

1. _____   5. _____   9. _____

2. _____   6. _____   10. _____

3. _____   7. _____   11. _____

4. _____   8. _____   12. _____

Say the name of the picture. **Circle** its name.

1.
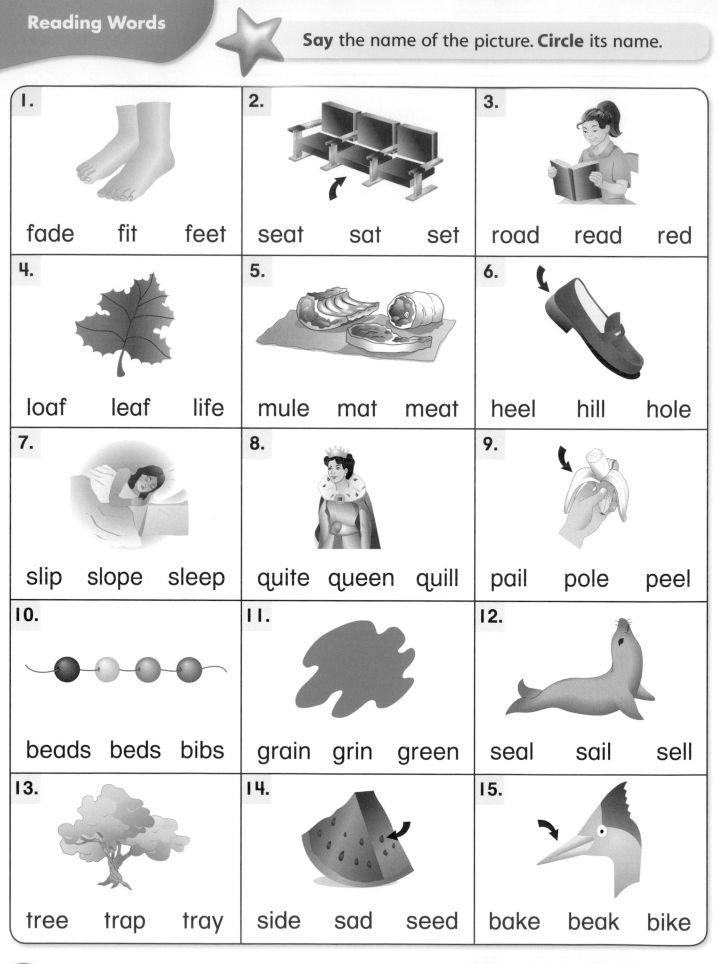
fade   fit   feet

2.
seat   sat   set

3.
road   read   red

4.
loaf   leaf   life

5.
mule   mat   meat

6.
heel   hill   hole

7.
slip   slope   sleep

8.
quite   queen   quill

9.
pail   pole   peel

10.
beads   beds   bibs

11.
grain   grin   green

12.
seal   sail   sell

13.
tree   trap   tray

14.
side   sad   seed

15.
bake   beak   bike

PHONICS ALIVE AT HOME

Randomly read the words on the page. Have your child tap his or her feet when he or she hears a long **e** word.

_____

_____

_____

⭐ **Say** the name of the picture. **Circle** its name and **print** it on the line.

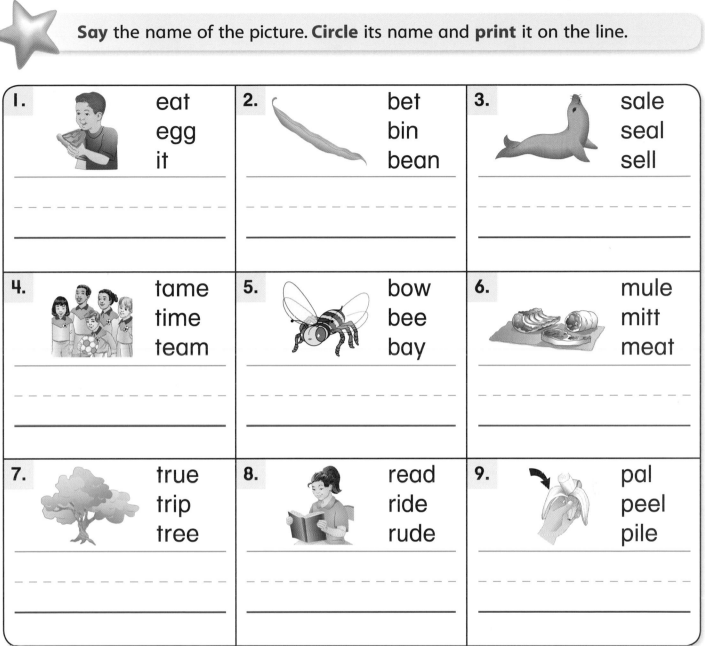

1.		eat egg it	2.		bet bin bean	3.		sale seal sell
4.		tame time team	5.		bow bee bay	6.		mule mitt meat
7.		true trip tree	8.		read ride rude	9.		pal peel pile

⭐ **Write** a sentence about one picture. Use a long **e** word.

_____

_____

_____

_____

 Visit **www.sadlierphonicsonline.com** for another long e activity.

Lesson 132 • Writing Long Vowel **e**

237

Read the name of the picture. **Circle L** if you hear long **e. Circle S** if you hear short **e. Color** the picture if it has the long **e** sound.

1. beads
L   S

2. bed
L   S

3. ten
L   S

4. meat
L   S

5. feet
L   S

6. beg
L   S

7. men
L   S

8. peas
L   S

9. desk
L   S

10. pet
L   S

11. beak
L   S

12. read
L   S

13. hen
L   S

14. bee
L   S

15. sled
L   S

16. team
L   S

PHONICS ALIVE AT HOME

Ask your child to read the long e words, stretching out the long e sound like this: **f-e-e-e-e-t.**

8 Wow! Now you see leaves and a stem. Isn't that neat?

Read

Name _____

A Bean Seed

You can grow a bean. This is a bean seed. 1

6 Keep the bean seed wet. Water it three times a week.

Make a deep hole in the dirt. This hole is for the seed. 3

DIRECTIONS: Cut and fold the book. Read the story. If you come to a word you don't know, sound it out by looking at each letter. Tell how to grow a bean plant.

Lesson 133 • Long Vowel **e** Reader Comprehension: Identifying Steps in a Process

239

Find a clay pot. Fill the pot
2 with dirt.

What do you see? Is it
something green? 7

Put the bean seed in the hole.
4 Then cover up the seed.

Set the pot in the sun.
Keep your eye on it. 5

Work Together **Look** at the picture. **Circle** the word that completes the sentence. **Print** it on the line. Take turns **reading** the sentences with a partner.

1.	Dee puts on her _____ _____ .	jets jams jeans
2.	Now she _____ _____ a bag.	needs nods nails
3.	She _____ _____ Uncle Bob.	mats meets mitts
4.	They go to the _____ _____ .	bait bell beach
5.	Each _____ _____ they meet there.	week wet wake
6.	They _____ _____ up the beach.	clip clay clean

 Visit **www.sadlierphonicsonline.com** for another long e activity.

Read Read the story. Use long **e** words from the story to complete the sentences.

In the Big Tree

Last week Dad and I
saw a big tree.
Dad said, "Stay still, Lee.
Listen to the birds peep."

I looked up and saw
three baby birds in a nest.
Dad said, "Their mother will
bring them a nice meal."

1. Last _____ we saw a big tree.

2. We could hear the birds _____ .

3. I saw _____ baby birds in a nest.

4. Their mother will bring them a _____ .

PHONICS
ALIVE AT HOME

With your child, name three
things you can do together
that have the long e sound.

Read the story. **Print** three long **e** words from the story and three more long **e** words that you know. Then **read** all the words you wrote.

The Seals Win!

I sit in my seat.
I see Lee run!
I leap up.
I yell for the Seals.
"Go, Seals, go!"
Lee can see the goal line.
Do not stop, Lee!
Lee runs deep in the end zone.
The Seals win the game!

SEALS 13 CUBS 7

CUBS 33

CUBS 12

Story Words

1. _____

2. _____

3. _____

My Words

1. _____

2. _____

3. _____

Seeds, Trees, and Leaves!

The people need to take care of the park. **Write** about what you see. Use some long **e** words. **Look** at the words in the box if you need help.

keep	real	clean	neat	seed
tree	need	heap	see	team

PHONICS ALIVE AT HOME

Have your child read the long **e** words in the box. Ask him or her to think of a word that rhymes with each one.

 Check-Up

Say the name of the picture. If its name has the long **e** sound, find the letters in the box to complete the word. **Print** the letters on the line. Then **trace** the whole word.

ea	ee

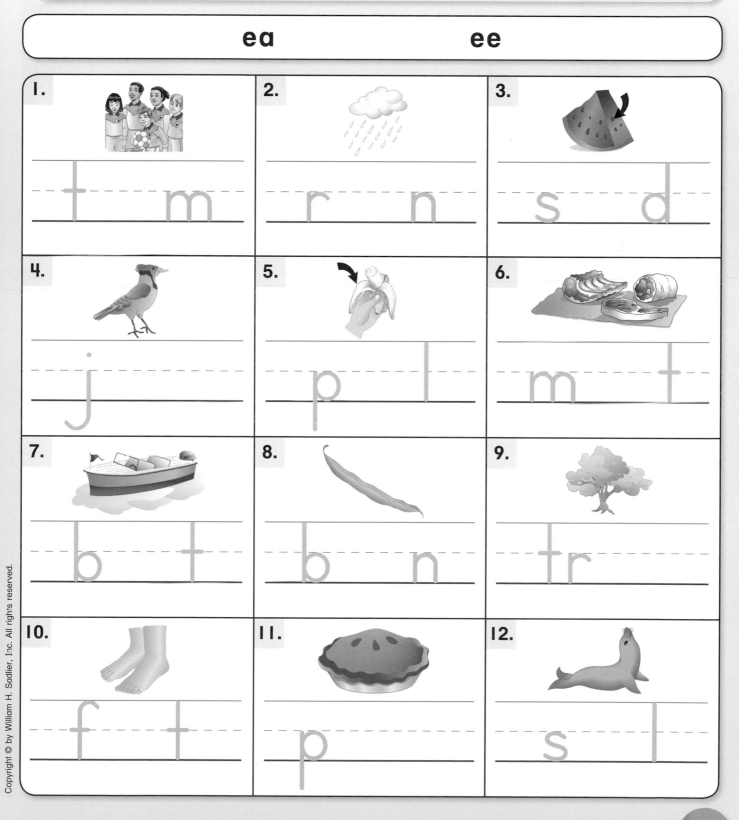

1. t __ m

2. r __ n

3. s __ d

4. j __

5. p __

6. m __ t

7. b __ t

8. b __ n

9. tr __

10. f __ t

11. p __

12. s __ l

Read the sentences. **Number** the sentences to tell the story in the correct order. **Print** the sentences in order on the lines.

_____ Then, she gave it water.

_____ Next, she put a pine tree in it.

_____ At last, she waits for it to grow.

_____ First, June made a hole.

1. _____ .

2. _____ .

3. _____ .

4. _____ .

 Visit **www.sadlierphonicsonline.com** for another activity with long vowels.

When **y** is at the end of a word, it can have the sound
of long **i**, as in **sky**, or the sound of long **e**, as in **bunny**.
Listen for the sounds of **y** in the rhyme.

Up in the sky,
see the clouds fly by.
One looks like a bunny.
Isn't that funny?

Say the name of the picture. **Circle** the picture if the **y** sound in its
name has the long **i** sound. **Draw** a line under the picture if the **y**
in its name has the long **e** sound.

sky

bunny

1.

2. 20

3.

4. 40

5.

6.

7.

8.

9.

10.

11.

Say the name of the picture. **Circle** its name and **print** it on the line.

1.
cherry
cry

2.
daisy
day

3.
buggy
by

4.
50
fifty
fly

5.
candy
cry

6.
silly
sky

7.
penny
pry

8.
play
fly

9.
pony
spy

10.
handy
dry

11.
baby
bay

12.
gray
fry

PHONICS ALIVE AT HOME

Count by tens to 100. Have your child repeat number words that end with the long e sound as in **thirty**.

Car has the **ar** sound. **Listen** for the sound of **ar** in the rhyme.

My mom could drive her car,
but she's not going too far.
So she'll just pass
and save all the gas!

The letter **r** after a vowel gives the vowel a new sound. **Say** the name of the picture. **Color** the picture if its name has the **ar** sound.

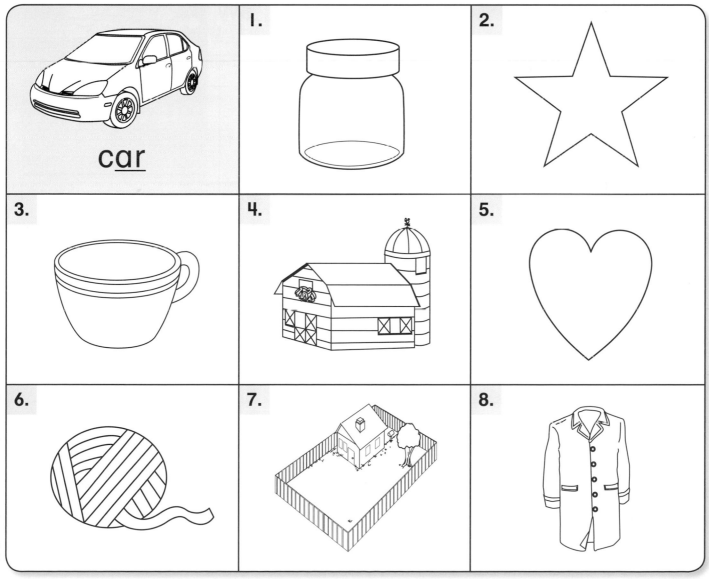

car

1.

2.

3.

4.

5.

6.

7.

8.

Say the name of each picture. **Circle** the pictures whose names have the **ar** sound. **Print ar** on the line.

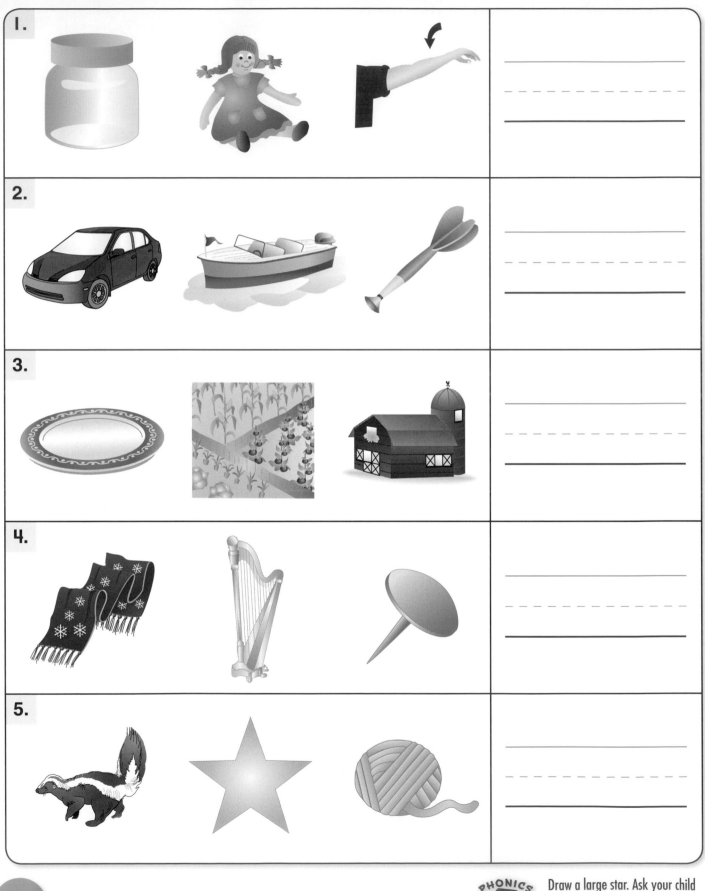

1.

2.

3.

4.

5.

PHONICS ALIVE AT HOME

Draw a large star. Ask your child to write **ar** words inside it, such as **car** and **park.**

Corn has the **or** sound.
Listen for the sound of **or** in the rhyme.

Corn, corn, it's very good—
I really like to eat it.
On the cob or with a fork—
you truly can not beat it!

Say the name of each picture. **Circle** the pictures that have the **or** sound.

Remember that **r** after a vowel gives it a new sound. **Say** the name of the picture. **Print or** if it has the **or** sound. Then **trace** the whole word.

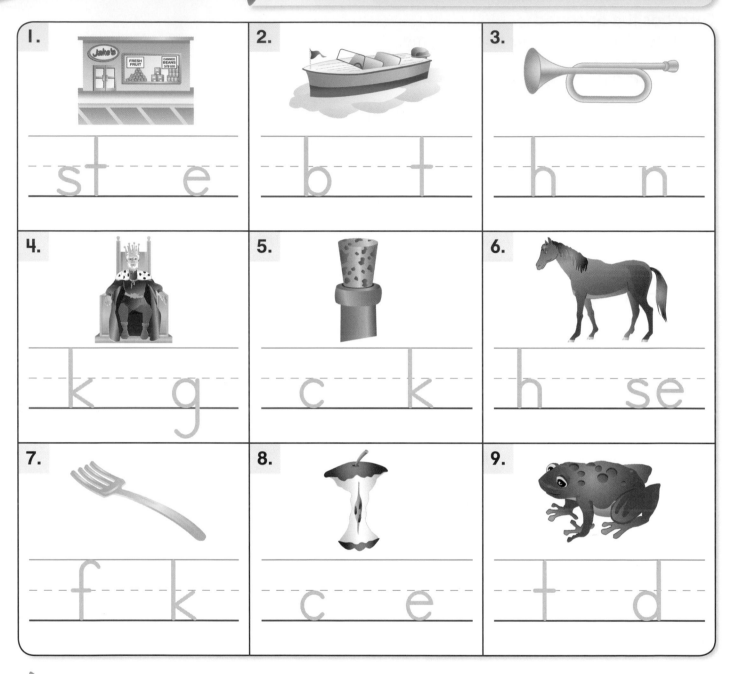

1. s t ___ e

2. b ___ t

3. h ___ n

4. k ___ g

5. c ___ k

6. h ___ se

7. f ___ k

8. c ___ e

9. t ___ d

Write a sentence about one of the pictures. Use an **or** word.

PHONICS
ALIVE AT HOME

Read one of your child's favorite books together. As you read, help your child find words in the story with the sound of **or**.

Turn has the sound of **ur**. **Listen** for this sound in the rhyme.

A hot air balloon trip—
We had the nerve to take a turn first.
We sure hope this balloon
doesn't rip or burst!

Say the name of each picture. **Circle** the pictures that have the same sound heard in the middle of **turn.**

1.

2.

3.

4.

5.

Work Together

Say the name of the picture with a partner.
Circle the letters that stand for the missing sound.
Print the letters. Then **trace** the whole word.

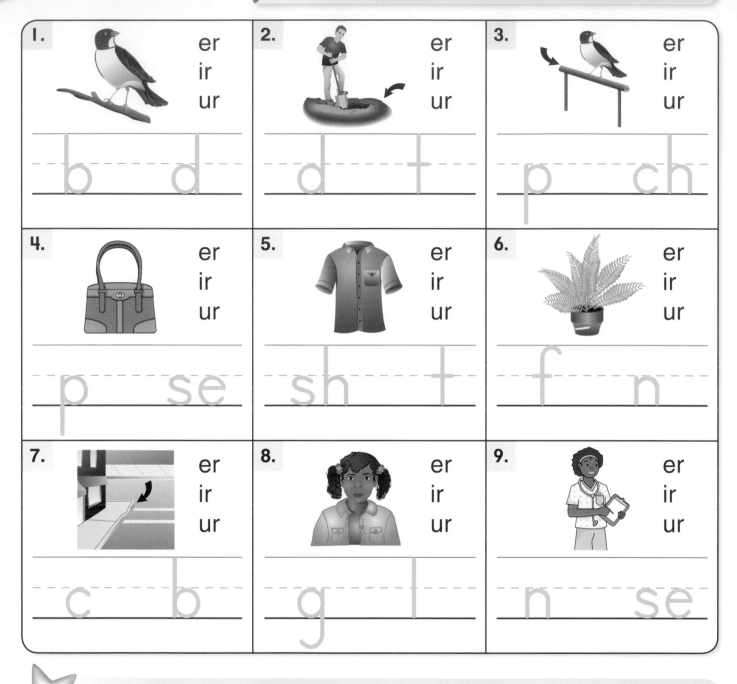

1. er ir ur
    b ___ d

2. er ir ur
    d ___ t

3. er ir ur
    p ___ ch

4. er ir ur
    p ___ se

5. er ir ur
    sh ___ t

6. er ir ur
    f ___ n

7. er ir ur
    c ___ b

8. er ir ur
    g ___ l

9. er ir ur
    n ___ se

Write the answers. Use an **er, ir,** or **ur** word.

10. This person helps you when you are sick. _____

11. This animal can fly. _____

PHONICS ALIVE AT HOME Draw a circle. Help your child think of words with **er, ir,** and **ur** and write them inside the circle.

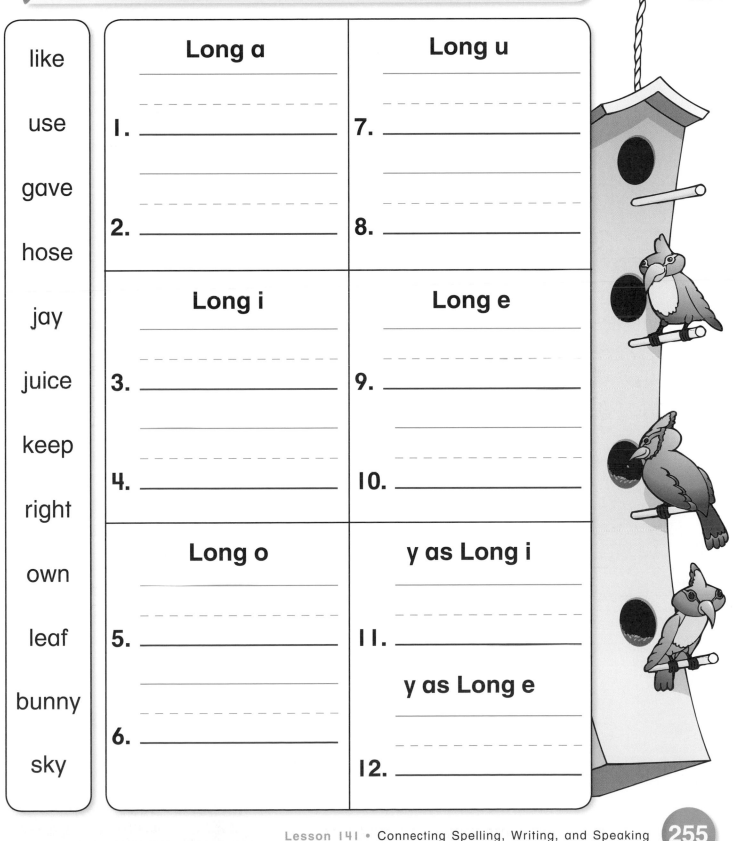

Spell, Write, and Tell

Say, **spell**, and **talk** about each word in the box.
Print each word under the vowel sound in its name.

like

use

gave

hose

jay

juice

keep

right

own

leaf

bunny

sky

Long a

1. _____

2. _____

Long u

7. _____

8. _____

Long i

3. _____

4. _____

Long e

9. _____

10. _____

Long o

5. _____

6. _____

y as Long i

11. _____

y as Long e

12. _____

Spell, Write, and Tell — **Write** notes to Jake and Lane and tell them how to be kind to Earth. Use one or more of the words in the box. **Share** what you wrote.

like	gave	jay	keep	own	right
use	hose	juice	bunny	leaf	sky

To Jake: _____

_____

_____

_____

_____

To Lane: _____

_____

_____

_____

_____

PHONICS ALIVE AT HOME — With your child, think of one way your family can be kinder to Earth. Use one of the spelling words in your idea.

Read Use one of the words in the box to complete each sentence. **Read** the sentences aloud.

| down | How | little | Please | Put | said |

1.

"_____

I said, _____ help the sea ."

2.

_____

Keep the _____ safe.

3.

_____

Mom _____, "Please help the ."

4.

_____

Do not cut _____ .

5.

_____

_____ can you help save the ?

6.

_____

_____ that in a bin.

Circle the word in the box that completes each sentence. **Print** the word on the line. **Read** the sentences.

1. Mike and Kate _____ and help.	stop said
2. Kate _____ pick up the cans.	down will
3. Mike will _____ the cans in a bin.	little put
4. Dad will _____ his bike.	how ride
5. How will you _____ ?	please help

☺ help   ☺ stop   ☺ little   ☺ ride   ☺ will

☺ down   ☺ put   ☺ how   ☺ said   ☺ please

PHONICS ALIVE AT HOME Have your child make up sentences that use the words in the Check-Up box.

Look at the pictures. **Read** the page. **Talk** about what you see.

Learn About Earth

Earth is our home.
It gives us nice things
like pine trees, blue lakes,
fruit to eat, and green grass.
We must take care of Earth.
We must keep it safe and clean.

How are the people in the
pictures helping Earth?
How can you help Earth?

WE RECYCLE

In the Yard

The girl is helping her mom in the yard. **Write** about what you see. Use some words with **r**-controlled vowels. **Look** at the words in the box if you need help.

yard	dirt	girl	bird	fern
her	porch	corn	hurt	turn

Lesson 144 • Writing **r**-Controlled Vowels in Context

PHONICS ALIVE AT HOME

Have your child read the words in the box. Ask him or her to identify the letters that stand for the **r**-controlled vowel in each word. Then have him or her say the sound the **r**-controlled vowel makes.

Check-Up **Fill in** the circle next to the name of the picture.

1. ○ sail ○ seal ○ sell

2. ○ glum ○ glue ○ glow

3. ○ flip ○ fly ○ flow

4. ○ pile ○ pal ○ peel

5. 50 ○ fit ○ fat ○ fifty

6. ○ am ○ arm ○ aim

7. ○ tame ○ team ○ ten

8. ○ suit ○ sit ○ seat

9. ○ mile ○ mule ○ mail

10. ○ high ○ heat ○ hay

11. ○ rose ○ raise ○ rise

12. ○ pea ○ pay ○ pie

13. ○ car ○ core ○ coat

14. ○ bike ○ beak ○ bake

15. ○ bill ○ bail ○ bowl

⭐ **Check-Up** **Fill in** the circle next to the name of the picture.

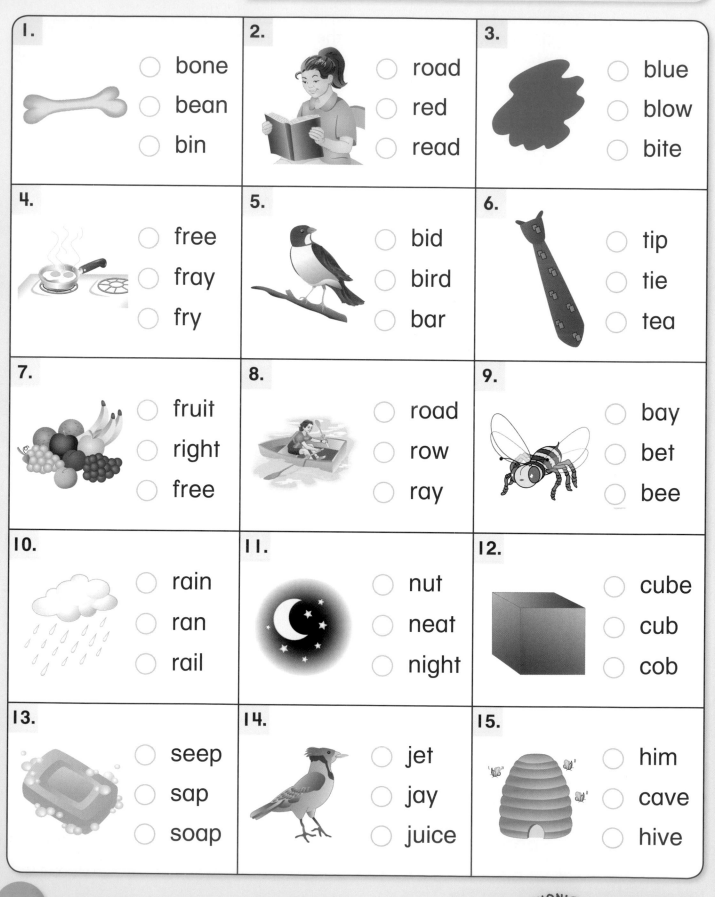

1.
- ○ bone
- ○ bean
- ○ bin

2.
- ○ road
- ○ red
- ○ read

3.
- ○ blue
- ○ blow
- ○ bite

4.
- ○ free
- ○ fray
- ○ fry

5.
- ○ bid
- ○ bird
- ○ bar

6.
- ○ tip
- ○ tie
- ○ tea

7.
- ○ fruit
- ○ right
- ○ free

8.
- ○ road
- ○ row
- ○ ray

9.
- ○ bay
- ○ bet
- ○ bee

10.
- ○ rain
- ○ ran
- ○ rail

11.
- ○ nut
- ○ neat
- ○ night

12.
- ○ cube
- ○ cub
- ○ cob

13.
- ○ seep
- ○ sap
- ○ soap

14.
- ○ jet
- ○ jay
- ○ juice

15.
- ○ him
- ○ cave
- ○ hive

 PHONICS ALIVE AT HOME Review this Check-Up with your child.

Name _____

We Can Take Care of the Earth

Reading at Home: Read the book together. Have your child retell the story using his or her own words. Then find and read the long vowel words, such as **see** and **nice**.

Fold

3

We clean up a stream.
We can plant trees beside it.

Fold

President of the United States
The White House
Washington, DC 20502

We can learn the rules and tell what we know. Please write to someone who can help.

8

We can turn off the water while we brush our teeth.

6

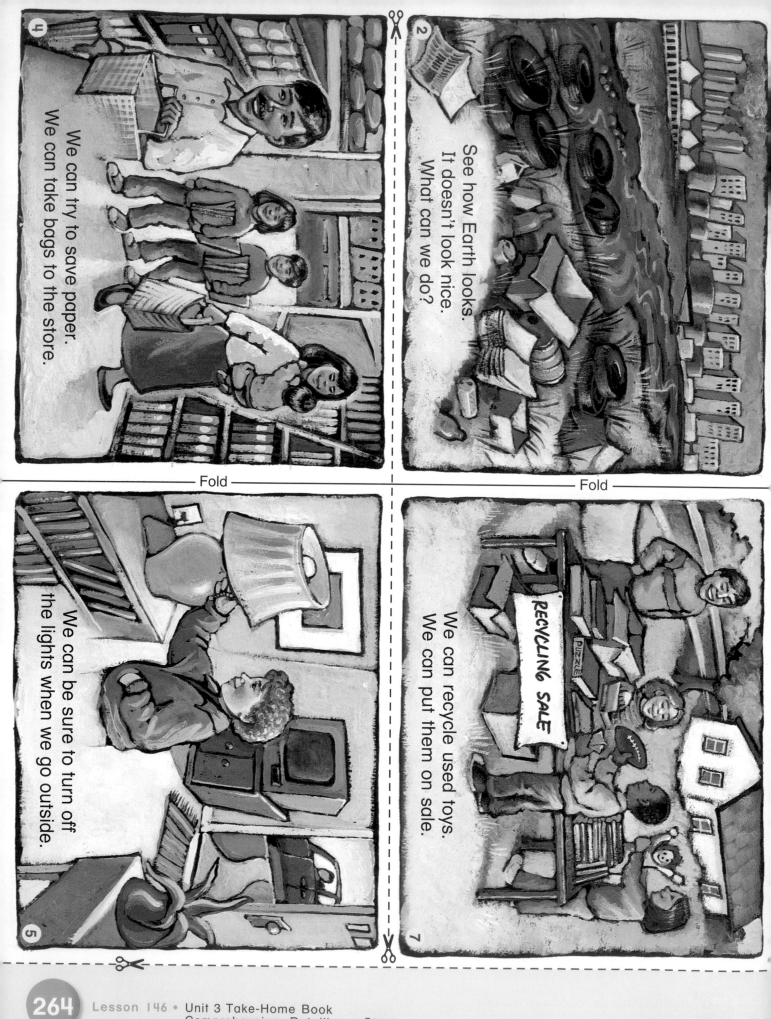

4

We can try to save paper.
We can take bags to the store.

2

See how Earth looks.
It doesn't look nice.
What can we do?

Fold

Fold

5

We can be sure to turn off
the lights when we go outside.

7

We can recycle used toys.
We can put them on sale.

RECYCLING SALE

PUZZLE

Play starts with the **l** blend **pl**. **Listen** for the sounds of **l** blends in the rhyme.

When I play ball, it's noisy.
I slide and the fans all clap.
But please be quiet now.
I'm going to take a nap.

Say the name of the pictures in each row. **Circle** and **color** each picture that has the same **l** blend as the picture in the box.

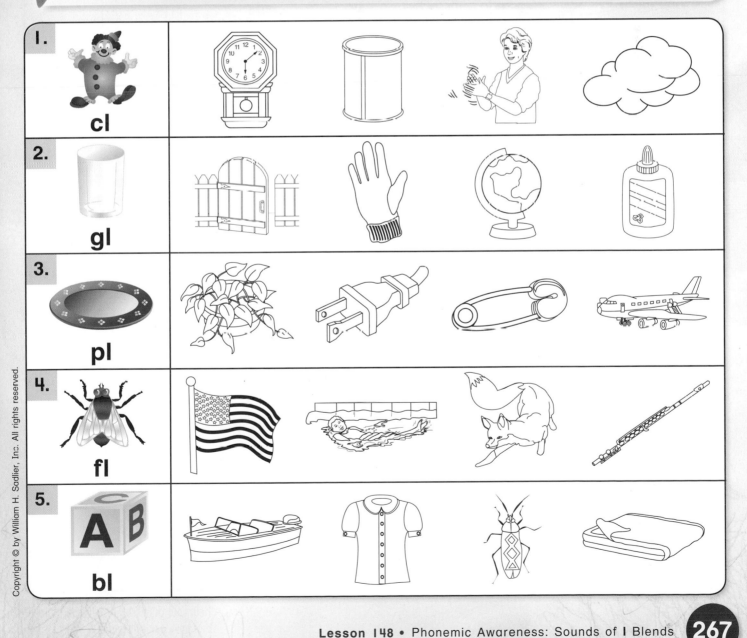

Sound to Symbol

Blue, glue, plane, and **flag** begin with l blends.
Color the pictures if their names begin with
bl ✏️, gl ✏️, pl ✏️, or fl ✏️.

bl   **gl**   **pl**   **fl**

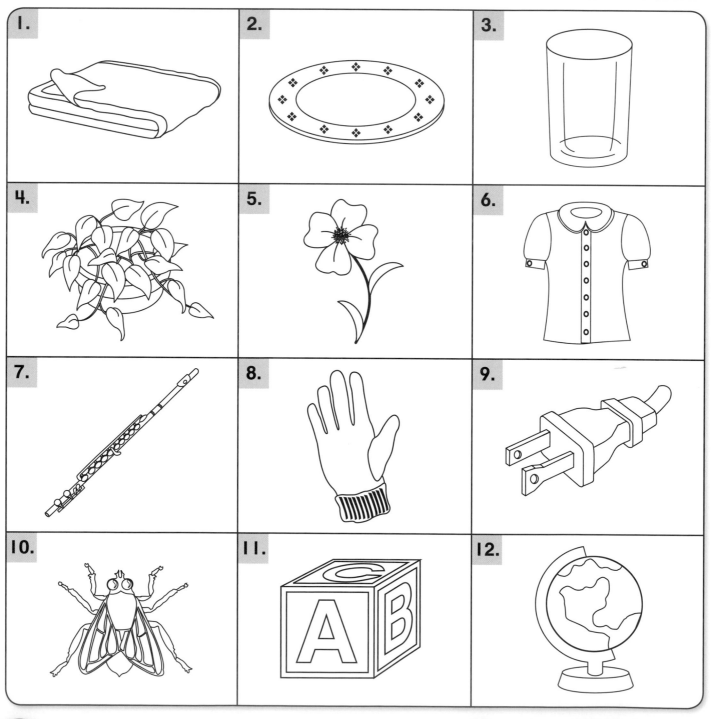

1.

2.

3.

4.

5.

6.

7.

8.

9.

10.

11.

12.

268 **Lesson 148** • Practicing l Blends

PHONICS ALIVE AT HOME Help your child list things in your home that have names beginning with l blends, such as **floors** and **plants**.

Work Together **Say** the name of the picture with a partner. **Circle** the word and **print** it on the line.

1. flat fit feet	2. bell bee blue	3. cape clap cap
4. back bake block	5. pine plane pan	6. flute fell fin
7. club cub cube	8. late pat plate	9. flag frog fig

Write a sentence about one picture. Use a word that begins with an **l** blend.

Read the poem. **Draw** a line under the words that begin with l blends. **Write** a complete sentence to answer each question.

Our Senses

Hear the wind blow.
See the blue sky.
Hear the clock tick
and the loud, buzzing fly.

Feel the smooth glass.
Smell the sweet flower.
Hear the plane roar
as it flies by the tower.

1. What can you smell?

_____

_____

_____

_____

2. What can you feel?

_____

_____

_____

_____

Lesson 149 • Words with l Blends in Context
Comprehension: Making Generalizations

Sit with your child and talk about what you hear, see, feel, smell, and taste. Write down any words that start with an l blend.

Dragon starts with the **r** blend **dr. Listen** for
the sounds of **r** blends in the rhyme.

Watch the dragon fly.
Feel his wings brush by.
Try to ride him if you dare.
Friendly dragons never care.

Say the name of the pictures in each row. **Circle** and **color** each picture
that has the same **r** blend as the picture in the box.

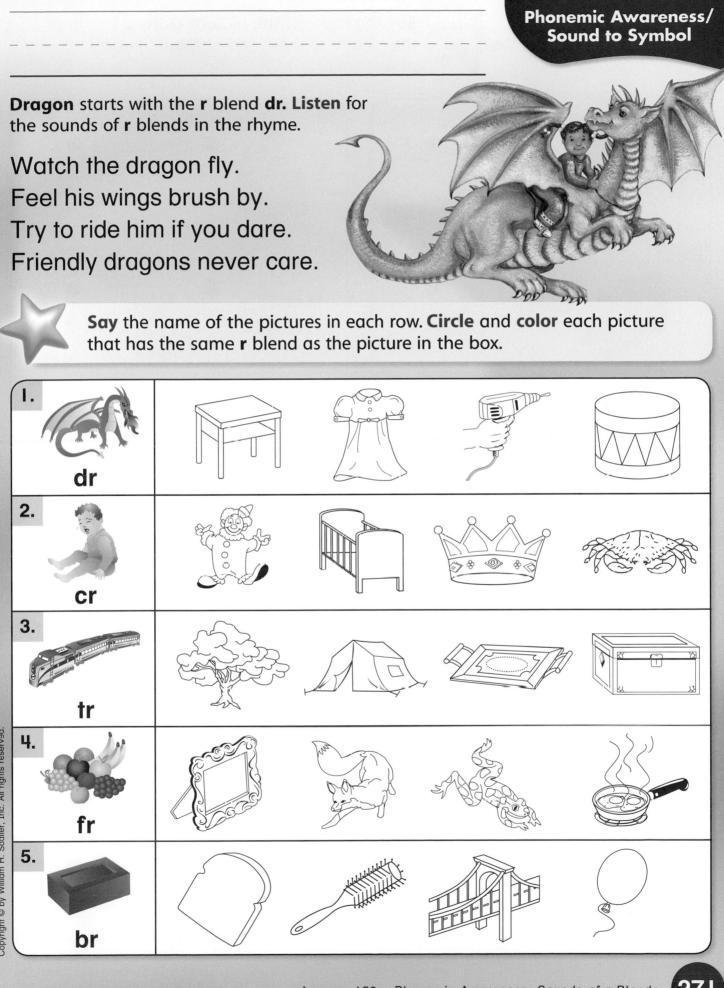

1. dr

2. cr

3. tr

4. fr

5. br

Say the name of the picture. **Draw** a line from the picture to the blend at the beginning of its name.

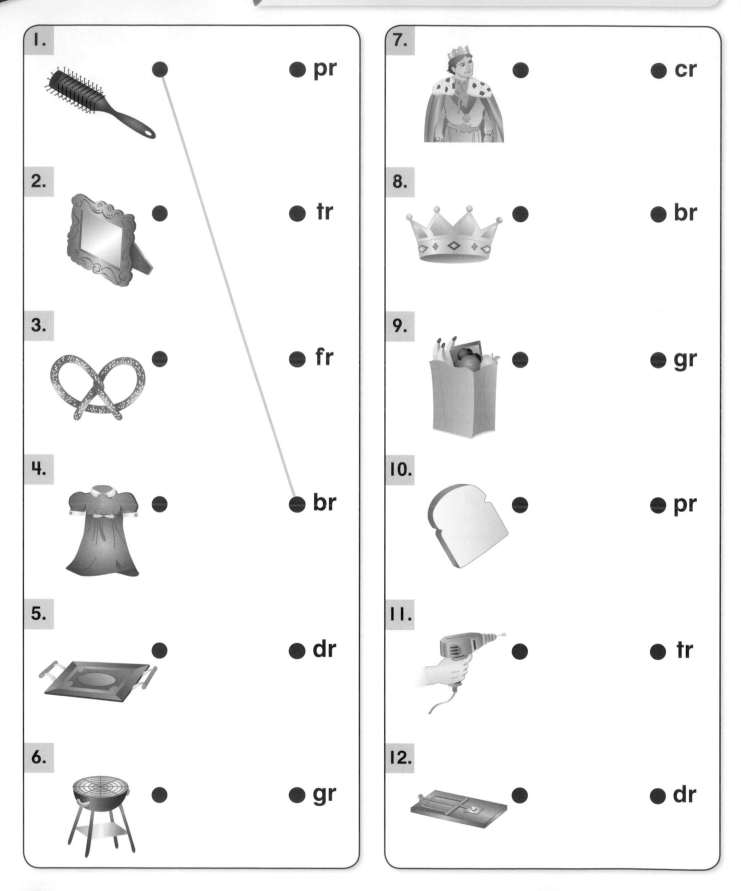

1.
● pr

2.
● tr

3.
● fr

4.
● br

5.
● dr

6.
● gr

7.
● cr

8.
● br

9.
● gr

10.
● pr

11.
● tr

12.
● dr

PHONICS ALIVE AT HOME Randomly name the pictures. Have your child say and spell the beginning blend.

Work Together

Say the name of the picture with a partner. **Circle** the word and **print** it on the line.

1. flag fog frog	**2.** prize plays pies	**3.** doll drum dime
4. club crab cab	**5.** bride ride block	**6.** globe get green
7. rail drill dig	**8.** rain train tail	**9.** tie tire tree

Write a sentence about one picture. Use a word that begins with an **r** blend.

Read the poem. **Draw** a line under the words that begin with **r** blends. **Write** a complete sentence to answer each question.

Read

Tasty Treats

I like the taste of bread and jam,
and crunchy pretzels, fruit, and ham,
refried frijoles—tacos, too.
And I love fresh green grapes, don't you?
And frozen yogurt—what a treat!
It's great to end with something sweet.

I. Which of the treats are crunchy?

_____

_____

_____

2. Which of the treats are sweet?

_____

_____

_____

PHONICS ALIVE AT HOME Help your child make a list of healthy treats. Have him or her circle any words that begin with **r** blends.

Spaghetti starts with the **s** blend **sp. Listen** for the sounds of **s** blends in the rhyme.

I love spaghetti.
It's my special treat.
It's good when it's spicy,
and sloppy to eat.

Say the name of the pictures in each row. **Circle** each picture that has the same **s** blend as the picture in the box.

1. sl

2. st

3. sp

4. sk

5. sw

Say the name of the picture. **Circle** the letters that stand for the beginning **s** blend in the picture name.

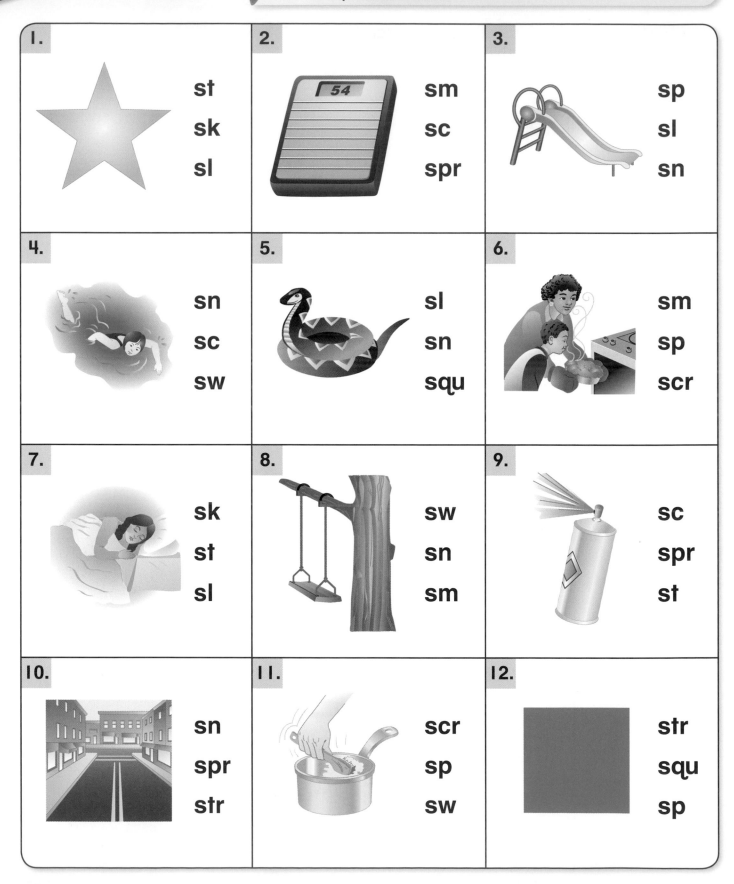

1. st / sk / sl

2. sm / sc / spr

3. sp / sl / sn

4. sn / sc / sw

5. sl / sn / squ

6. sm / sp / scr

7. sk / st / sl

8. sw / sn / sm

9. sc / spr / st

10. sn / spr / str

11. scr / sp / sw

12. str / squ / sp

PHONICS ALIVE AT HOME Draw the outline of a large star. Help your child write words inside the star that begin with **s** blends.

Work Together Say the name of the picture with a partner. **Circle** the word and **print** it on the line.

1. square / star / spare

2. sting / ring / string

3. swell / spill / seal

4. snail / nail / sail

5. spy / say / sky

6. slide / side / smile

7. wing / swing / sling

8. spray / stay / ray

9. sell / smell / spell

Write a sentence about one picture. Use a word that begins with an **s** blend.

Read the story. **Draw** a line under the words that begin with **s** blends. Then complete the sentences.

A Scarecrow Speaks

I like to stand in one spot.
I see spiders spin webs.
I hear the gate squeak.
Sometimes I sneak a sweet strawberry.
Some days rain sprinkles on me.
I like what I see, hear, taste, feel, and smell.
Oh, no! I do not like it now!
A smelly skunk is strolling my way.
Stop, skunk, stop!

1. The scarecrow sees spiders _____ webs.

2. The scarecrow hears the gate _____ .

3. The scarecrow sneaks a _____ strawberry.

4. The scarecrow will not like the smell of a _____ .

278 Lesson 153 • Words with **s** Blends in Context
Comprehension: Making Predictions

Have your child draw a picture of a scarecrow. Talk about the things you would use to make it.

Spell, Write, and Tell Say, **spell**, and **talk** about each word in the box. **Print** each word under the blend in its name. **Circle** the letters that spell the blend.

small

blue

grill

sweet

dry

glad

long

pretty

band

spin

went

clean

l Blends

1.

2.

3.

s Blends

7.

8.

9.

r Blends

4.

5.

6.

Final Blends

10.

11.

12.

Spell, Write, and Tell

Write a note to thank a friend for a great party. Use some of the words in the box. **Share** what you wrote.

small	grill	dry	long	band	went
blue	sweet	glad	pretty	spin	clean

Dear _____,

_____

_____

_____

_____

_____

_____

_____

_____

_____

Your friend,

_____

PHONICS ALIVE AT HOME Help your child write and mail or e-mail a note to a friend or relative.

Read Use one of the words in the box to complete each
sentence. **Read** the sentences aloud.

| again | ate | big | Look | to | yellow |

1.

Glen and Brad rode a bus _____ the _____ .

2.

Brad said, "I see a _____ ."

3.

Glen said, "I see a _____ ."

4.

Glen said, " _____ at the _____ ."

5.

Brad said, "I _____ a _____ ."

6.

Glen and Brad will ride the bus _____ .

Visit **www.sadlierphonicsonline.com**
for another high-frequency words activity.

Lesson 156 • Reading High-Frequency Words

283

Circle the word in the box that completes each sentence. **Print** the word on the line. **Read** the sentences.

1. _____ I get the blue and _____ paint.	yellow said
2. _____ It is in a _____ jar.	ate big
3. _____ I paint a _____ yellow frog.	please funny
4. _____ Will you _____ at my yellow frog?	look to
5. _____ I will paint a frog _____ !	again see

Check-Up   **Color** a ☺ for each word you wrote.

☺ ate   ☺ look   ☺ said   ☺ please   ☺ funny

☺ big   ☺ see   ☺ to   ☺ again   ☺ yellow

PHONICS ALIVE AT HOME   Have your child read the words in the Check-Up box. Ask him or her to make up sentences with the words.

READ

Look at the pictures. **Read** the page.
Talk about what you see.

Learn About Senses

Most people have five senses.
We can see, hear, smell,
taste, and feel. We use
our senses all the time.

Look at the pictures.
Do you see red and blue?
Pretend you are playing the game.
What sound does the crowd make?
Does the mitt feel smooth?
What can you smell?
Wouldn't some crunchy popcorn and
a cool drink taste good right now?

Using all your senses
is fun. Try it!

Lesson 157 • Words with Consonant Blends in Context
Comprehension: Classifying Objects
Modeling Fluency

Best Friends

The friends are glad to be together. **Write** about what you see.
Use some words with initial and final blends. **Look** at the words in
the box if you need help.

frog	snail	crab	smell	roast
drink	sing	play	tent	sleep

PHONICS ALIVE AT HOME Have your child read the words in the box and identify the beginning and ending blends.

Use the picture clues to **fill in** the puzzle. **Print** one letter in each box.

ACROSS ➡

2.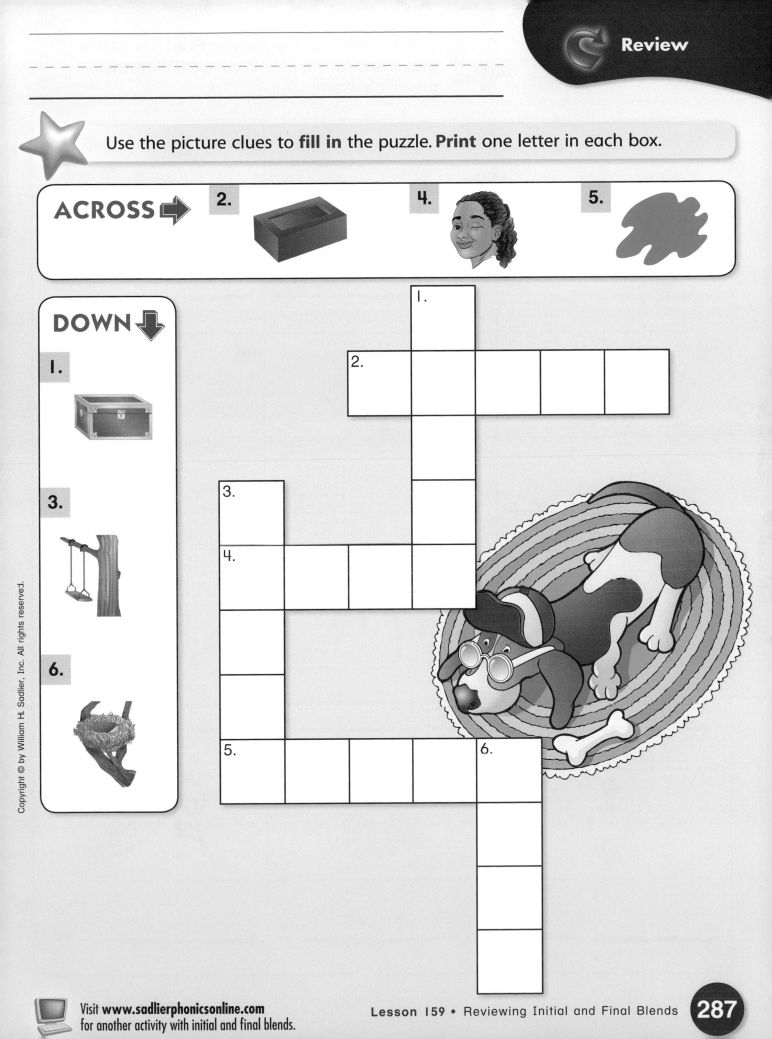

4.

5.

DOWN ⬇

1.

3.

6.

Visit **www.sadlierphonicsonline.com**
for another activity with initial and final blends.

Lesson 159 • Reviewing Initial and Final Blends

287

Check-Up **Say** the name of the picture. **Print** the letters that stand for the missing blend. Then **trace** the whole word.

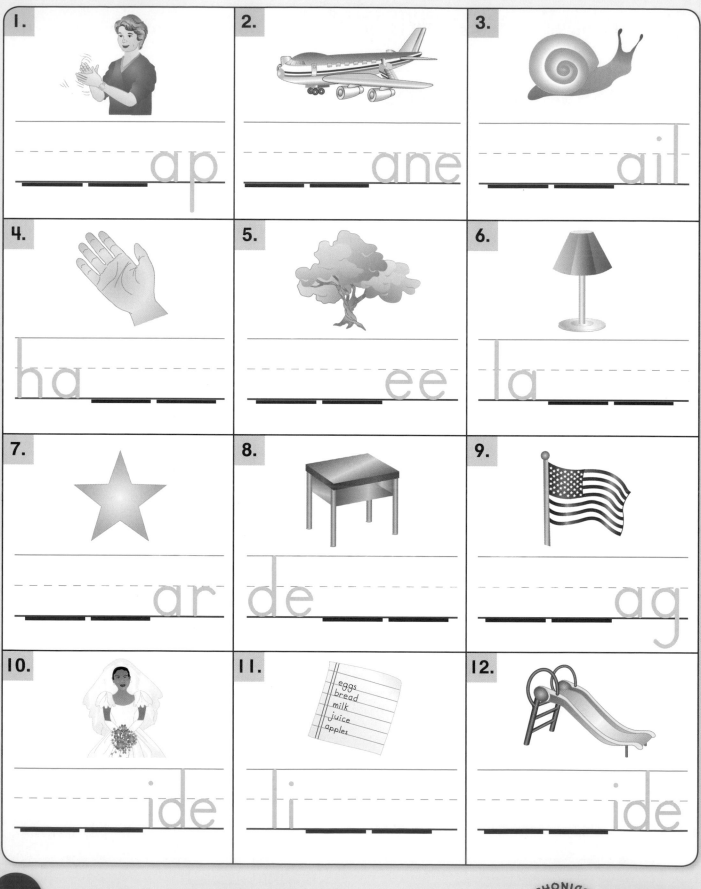

1. ____ ap

2. ____ ane

3. ____ ail

4. ha ____

5. ____ ee

6. la ____

7. ____ ar

8. de ____

9. ____ ag

10. ____ ide

11. li ____

12. ____ ide

PHONICS ALIVE AT HOME Review this Check-Up with your child.

Making Sense

Name _____

—1

Reading at Home: Read the book together. As you answer the questions, decide which answers are facts and which are opinions. Then find the pictures that have blends in their names, such as **plane** and **grapes**.

Fold

3

What sounds loud?

Fold

What smells good?

It looks _____

It feels _____

It is a _____

8

6

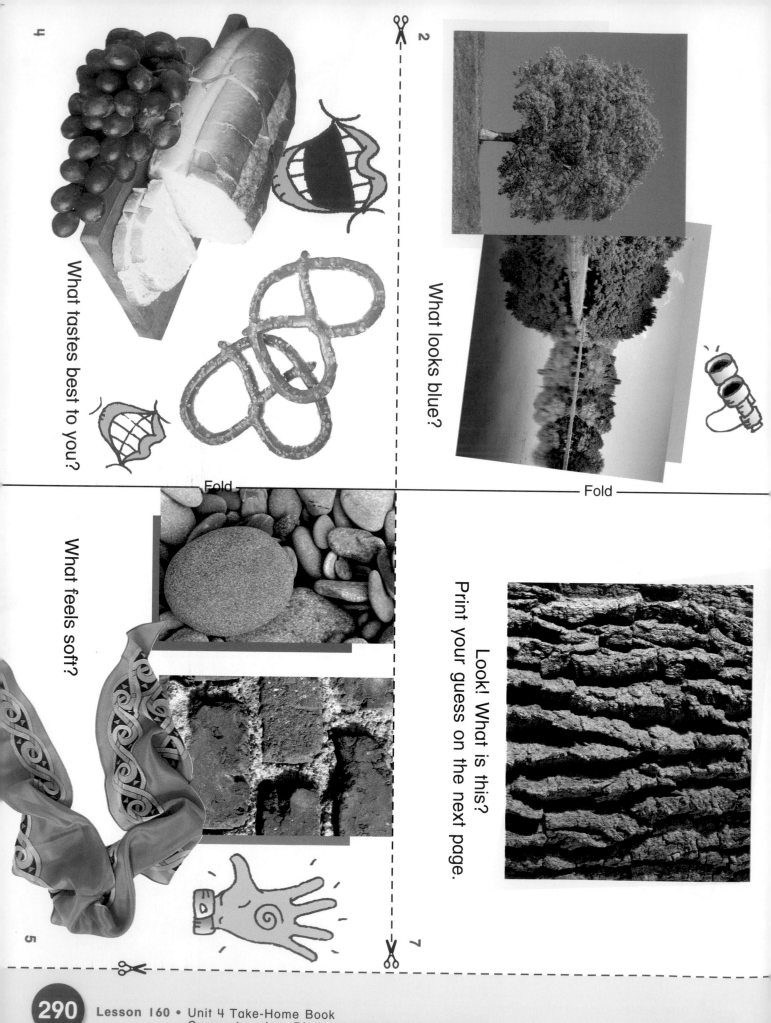

4

What tastes best to you?

2

What looks blue?

Fold

What feels soft?

Fold

Look! What is this?
Print your guess on the next page.

5

7

Comprehension: Distinguishing Fact and Opinion

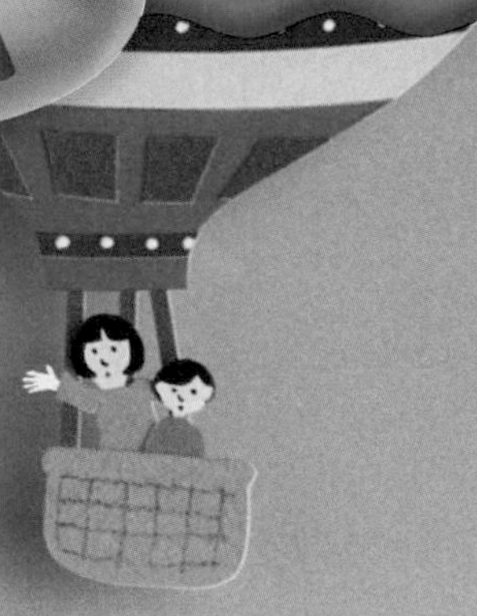

CLOUDS

White sheep, white sheep
On a blue hill,
When the wind stops
You all stand still.
When the wind blows
You walk away slow.
White sheep, white sheep,
Where do you go?

Christina G. Rossetti

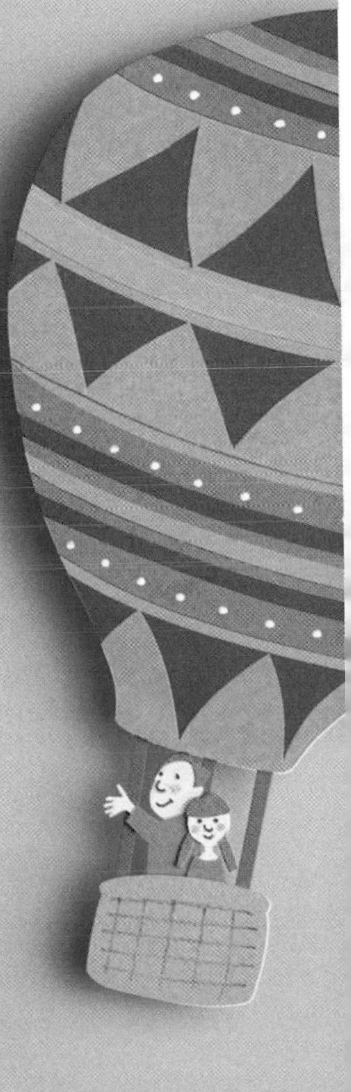

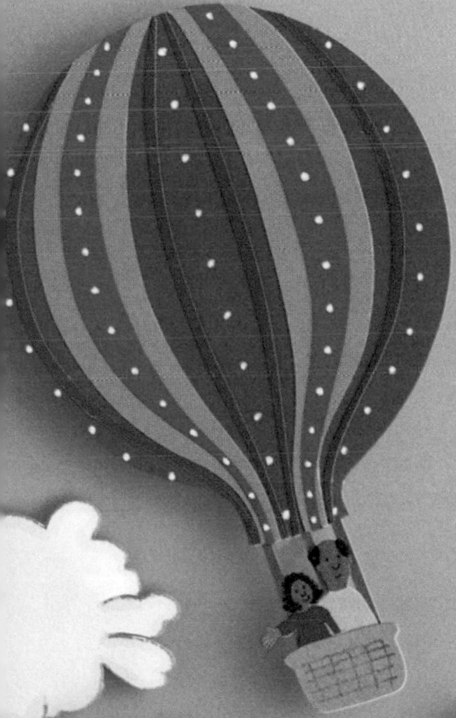

Oral Language How would the clouds look on a stormy day?
What do the different kinds of clouds tell you about the weather?

Name _____

Dear Family,

In this unit about weather, your child will learn the sounds of consonant digraphs. You can participate with your child by doing these home activities.

• Say the name of each picture below with your child. Listen to the sounds of the consonant digraphs **th, sh, wh, ch**, and **ck**.

Apreciada Familia:

En esta unidad se hablará del tiempo y se enseñarán los sonidos dígrafos de las consonantes. Pueden practicarlos con su hijo haciendo estas actividades en casa.

• Pronuncien el nombre de los objetos en los cuadros. Escuchen los sonidos dígrafos de las consonantes **th, sh, wh, ch** y **ck**.

th	**sh**	**wh**	**ch**	**ck**
thumb	sheep	whale	cherry	lock

• Read the poem "Clouds" on the reverse side of this page.

• Talk about the shapes of clouds you see in the sky. What do they remind you of?

• Help your child find words with consonant digraphs in the poem, such as **white, sheep, when,** and **where.** Then find the rhyming words. **(hill/still, slow/go)**

• Lean el poema "Clouds" en la página 291.

• Hablen de las diferentes formas de las nubes en el cielo. ¿Qué les recuerdan?

• Ayuden al niño a encontrar consonantes de sonido dígrafo en el poema, tales como: **white, sheep, when** y **where.** Después encuentren las palabras que riman. **(hill/still, slow/go)**

PROJECT

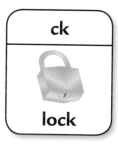

With your child, read and answer these questions about weather. **Wh**at is the weather like **wh**ere you live? Can you **th**ink of the sound that **th**under makes? Can you find a **sh**adow during a rain **sh**ower? If you had the **ch**ance, how would you **ch**ange the weather?

PROYECTO

Haga las siguientes preguntas sobre el tiempo al niño. ¿Cómo es el tiempo en el lugar donde vives? ¿Puedes imaginar el ruido que hace un trueno? ¿Puedes ver una sombra durante un aguacero? Si tuvieras la oportunidad ¿cómo cambiarías el tiempo?

292 Lesson 161 • Consonant Digraphs—Phonics Alive at Home

 Visit us at **www.sadlierphonicsonline.com**

th

Thunder starts with the sound of the consonant digraph **th**. **Listen** for the sound of **th** in the rhyme.

Think about thick clouds,
think about thunder.
Think of some big things
you can hide under.

Say the name of the picture. **Circle** the picture if its name starts with **th**.

1.

2.

3. 30

4.

5.

6. 10

7.

8.

9.

10.

11.

12.

Say the name of the picture. Circle **th** or **t** for each beginning sound. **Print** the word from the box that names the picture.

think   tape   thirty   tube   thorn
thumb   toe   thick   ten

1. th t

2. th t

3. 10 th t

4. th t

5. th t

6. th t

7. 30 th t

8. th t

9. th t

Write a sentence about one picture. Use a **th** word.

PHONICS ALIVE AT HOME

Read the words in the box. Ask your child to give the "thumbs up" sign after each **th** word.

sh

Shovel starts with the sound of the consonant digraph **sh**.
Listen for the sound of **sh** in the rhyme.

The sun is shining.
Shout hooray!
Grab a shovel.
Be on your way.

Say the name of the picture. **Circle** the letters that stand for the
beginning sound. **Circle** the picture if its name begins with **sh**.

1.	2.	3.	4.
sh th	sh th	sh th	sh th

5.	6.	7.	8.
sh th	sh th	sh th	sh th

9.	10.	11.	12.
sh th	sh th	sh th	sh th

Say the name of the picture. **Circle** its name and **print** the word. In the last box, draw a picture of an **sh** word. **Print** the word.

1. seed
    sad
    shed

2. shave
    save
    vase

3. hips
    safe
    shapes

4. shop
    stop
    drop

5. hurt
    short
    shirt

6. gift
    shelf
    soft

7. lake
    shake
    snake

8. ship
    hip
    sip

9.

Write a sentence about one picture. Use an **sh** word.

Read aloud all of the words. Have your child say "Shhh!" after each word that begins with the **sh** sound.

White starts with the sound of the consonant digraph **wh**.
Listen for the sound of **wh** in the rhyme.

Where did it come from?
When will it go?
This white whirly fog,
does anyone know?

Say the name of the picture. **Circle** the picture if its name starts with the sound of **wh**.

1.

2.

3.

4.

5.

6.

7.

8.

9.

10.

11.

12.

Work Together

Use a **wh** word from the box to complete each sentence. **Print** the word on the line. **Read** the sentences with a partner.

| white | What | whipped | When | Why |

1. _____ a bad weather day!

2. _____ I woke up, it was sunny.

3. Then the _____ clouds turned gray.

4. The wind _____ the leaves around.

5. _____ does it have to storm?

PHONICS
ALIVE AT HOME

Take turns with your child asking each other questions that begin with **What, When,** and **Why**.

Chilly starts with the sound of the consonant digraph **ch**.
Listen for the sound of **ch** in the rhyme.

SCHOOL #4

The air is so chilly.
It makes my teeth chatter,
but the weather keeps changing,
so what does it matter?

Say the name of the picture. **Circle** the picture if its name starts with the sound of **ch**.

1.	2.	3.	4.
5.	6.	7.	8.
9.	10.	11.	12.

Say the name of the picture. **Circle ch** or **c** for the beginning sound. **Print** the word from the box that names the picture.

chain	cap	cheek	chin	chop
chalk	coat	chick	cub	

1. ch c

2. ch c

3. ch c

4. ch c

5. ch c

6. ch c

7. ch c

8. ch c

9. ch c

Write a sentence about one picture. Use a **ch** word.

Lesson 165 • Connecting Sound to Symbol: /ch/ ch
Writing Consonant Digraph **ch**

PHONICS
ALIVE AT HOME

Have your child read the sentence to you. Then work together to make up sentences about other pictures.

Duck ends with the sound of consonant digraph **ck.**
Listen for words in the rhyme that end with the sound of **ck.**

The thunder came,
the storm, it struck.
I got so wet—
I felt like a duck!

Say the name of the picture. **Color** it if its name ends with the sound of **ck.**

Say the name of the picture. **Circle** its name and print it on the line.

1.
dab
dust
duck

_____

2.
try
truck
trip

_____

3.
lock
lake
tick

_____

4.
tack
tag
take

_____

5.
scat
chat
sock

_____

6.
chess
check
chain

_____

7.
cake
coach
kick

_____

8.
clock
luck
clog

_____

9.
rock
rest
track

_____

Write a sentence about one picture. Use a **ck** word.

_____

_____

PHONICS
ALIVE AT HOME

Play "I Know a Word." Take turns with your child naming words that end with **ck**.

Spell, Write, and Tell **Say**, **spell**, and **talk** about each word in the box. **Print** each word under the correct digraph.

thing	
sheep	
white	
chain	
back	
thin	
she	
clock	
think	
where	
chin	
shapes	

th

1. _____

2. _____

3. _____

sh

4. _____

5. _____

6. _____

wh

7. _____

8. _____

ch

9. _____

10. _____

ck

11. _____

12. _____

Spell, Write, and Tell

Pretend you are the pilot of a plane. **Write** about one of your trips. Use one or more of the words in the box. **Share** what you wrote.

thing

sheep

white

chain

back

thin

she

clock

think

where

chin

shapes

PHONICS ALIVE AT HOME

Sit with your child and pretend you are taking a plane ride together. Tell each other what you see.

Read Use one of the words in the box to complete each sentence. **Read** the sentences aloud.

come	find	open	out	want	We

1. I _____ to plan a  .

2. Dad and Gran will _____ , too.

3. _____ want to see if it will rain.

4. Gran can _____ out on .

5. Dad can find _____ in the .

6. I can _____ the to find out.

Circle the word in the box that completes each sentence. **Print** the word on the line. **Read** the sentences.

1. Matt _____ I go home.	open and
2. We _____ to get warm.	look want
3. We will _____ a game to play.	find said
4. We will _____ fun.	out have
5. Do you want to _____ too?	come little

Check-Up **Color** a 🙂 for each word you wrote.

🙂 open   🙂 little   🙂 look   🙂 have   🙂 and

🙂 want   🙂 said   🙂 out   🙂 come   🙂 find

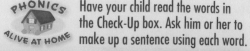

PHONICS ALIVE AT HOME — Have your child read the words in the Check-Up box. Ask him or her to make up a sentence using each word.

READ

Look at the pictures. Read the page. Talk about what you see.

Learn About Clouds

You know there are many kinds of clouds. They come in different shapes and colors.

Cumulus clouds are white and fluffy. You see them when the sun shines. Cirrus clouds look like feathers. When they are in the sky, the weather may change soon. A layer of stratus clouds can cover the sky. Stratus clouds may be gray and sometimes look almost black. They often bring rain.

When you go outside, check out the clouds. What are they telling you about the weather?

Cumulus Clouds

Cirrus Clouds

Stratus Clouds

Stuck in the Mud

Jack the Duck needs to get the rock out of the mud. **Write** about what you see. Use some words with **sh, ch, wh, th,** and **ck**. **Look** at the words in the box if you need help.

duck	rock	stuck	chick	chain
when	wheel	sheep	shake	think

Lesson 170 • Writing Consonant Digraphs in Context

PHONICS ALIVE AT HOME

Have your child read the words in the box. Then have him or her match the words he or she used in the story to the words in the box.

Read the riddles. **Print** the answers on the lines. The pictures will help you. **Circle** the words with consonant digraphs.

1. I grow on a tree.
I am a fruit you can pick.

I am a _____.

2. I swim in the sea,
but I am not a shark.

I am a _____.

3. I may prick you when
you pick a rose.

I am a _____.

4. I am black or white. I snack
in the shade with my flock.

I am a _____.

5. Use me on a door you shut.
You need a key to open me up.

I am a _____.

Visit **www.sadlierphonicsonline.com**
for another activity with consonant digraphs.

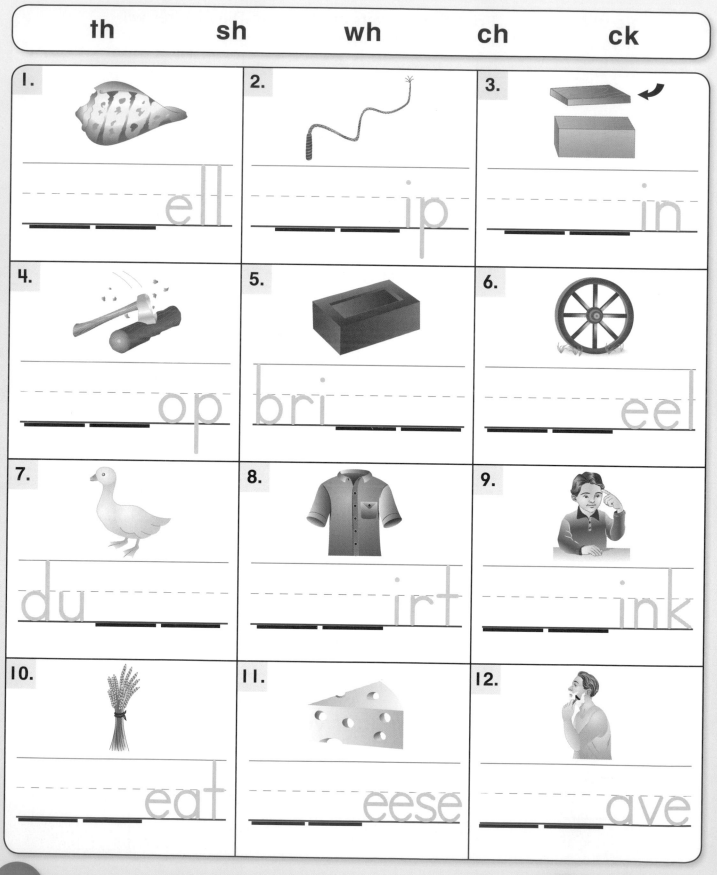

Check-Up

Say the name of the picture. **Find** the letters in the box that stand for the missing digraph and **print** them. Then **trace** the whole word.

| th | sh | wh | ch | ck |

1. ___ ell

2. ___ ip

3. ___ in

4. ___ op

5. bri ___

6. ___ eel

7. du ___

8. ___ irt

9. ___ ink

10. ___ eat

11. ___ eese

12. ___ ave

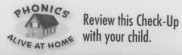

PHONICS ALIVE AT HOME
Review this Check-Up with your child.

Name —————

WEATHER CHANGES

Reading at Home: Read the book together. Talk about how you know when the weather is going to change. Then find words with **sh, th, ch, wh,** and **ck.**

————— Fold —————

③

Fold

Weather changes.
Storms dash by.
Soon it should be
warm and dry.

Thunder's knocking.
Crash and flash!
Rain is swishing.
Splish! Splash!

⑧

⑥

DIRECTIONS: Cut and fold the book.

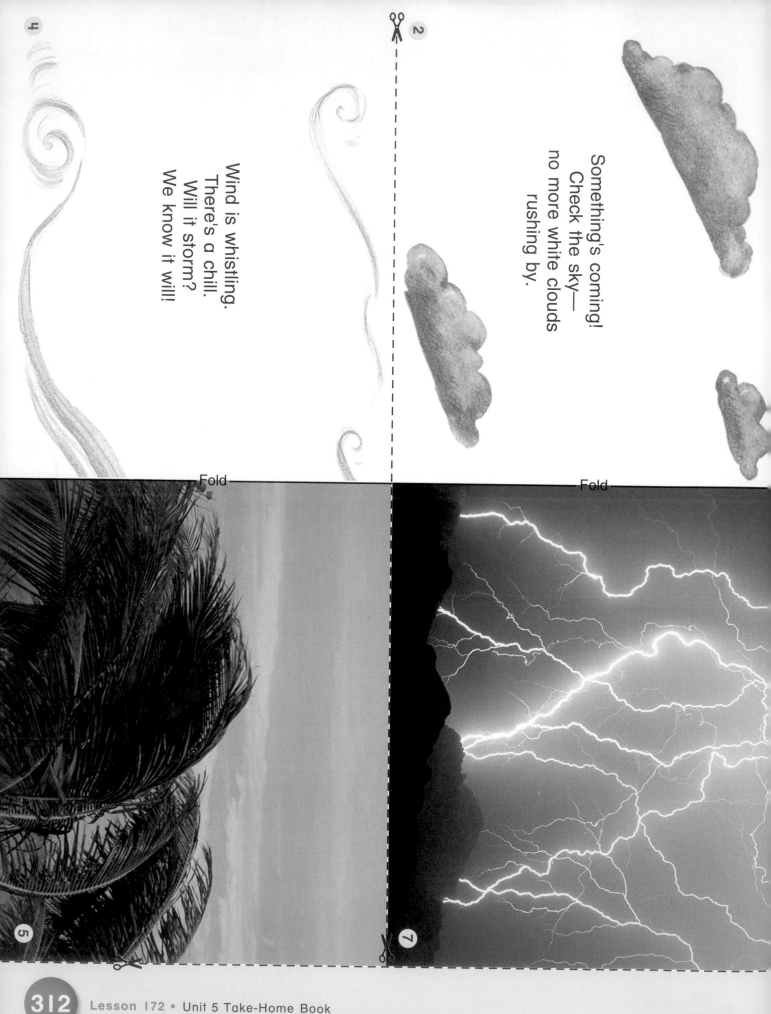

4

2 ✂

Something's coming!
Check the sky—
no more white clouds
rushing by.

Wind is whistling.
There's a chill.
Will it storm?
We know it will!

Fold

Fold

5

7 ✂

Lesson 172 • Unit 5 Take-Home Book
Comprehension: Drawing Conclusions

READ ALOUD

I put a seed into the ground
And said, "I'll watch it grow."
I watered it and cared for it
As well as I could know.

One day I walked in my back yard
And oh, what did I see!
My seed had popped itself right out,
Without consulting me.

Gwendolyn Brooks

Oral Language What would you do to help seeds grow?
What kind of seeds grow into big plants?

Dear Family,

As your child progresses through this unit, you can help phonics come alive at home. Your child will learn about things that grow, as well as words that "grow" from other words—compound words, contractions, and words with endings.

- Help your child read the words below.

Apreciada Familia:

A medida que los niños avanzan en esta unidad ustedes pueden revivir los fonemas en casa. Los niños aprenderán sobre el crecimiento de las cosas y también sobre palabras que "crecen" de otras palabras, palabras compuestas, contracciones y terminaciones.

- Ayuden al niño a leer estas palabras.

Compound Word Palabra compuesta	Contraction Contracción	Ending s Terminación s	Ending ing Terminación ing	Ending ed Terminación ed
sunflower	I'll	sees	growing	planted

- Read the poem "Tommy" on the reverse side of this page.

- Talk about things that grow, such as **flowers, kittens,** and, of course, **children.**

- Help your child find compound words in the poem **(itself, without),** the contraction **(I'll),** and words with endings **(watered, cared, walked, popped, consulting).**

- Then make a list of words that rhyme with **grow. (bow/go/hoe/mow/know/row/sow/toe)**

- Lean el poema "Tommy" en la página 313.

- Hablen de las cosas que crecen como las **flores, gatitos,** y por supuesto, **los niños.**

- Ayuden a su niño a encontrar palabras compuestas en el poema **(itself, without)** la contracción **(I'll)** y palabras con terminación **(watered, cared, walked, popped, consulting).**

- Después hagan una lista de palabras que riman con **grow. (bow/go/hoe/mow/know/row/sow/toe)**

PROJECT

With your child, draw a flower on paper and print **ing** in the center. Help your child make the flower "grow" by printing words with that ending in the petals. Draw another flower using the ending **s.**

PROYECTO

Dibujen una flor y escriban **ing** en el centro. Ayuden a su hijo a hacer "crecer" la flor escribiendo palabras con esa terminación en los pétalos. Dibujen otra flor usando la terminación **s.**

basket + ball = basketball

A compound word is a word made from two or more shorter words. **Basketball** is a compound word.
Listen and **look** for compound words in the rhyme.

I crawled in my playpen
when I was small.
Now I climb to the treetops
and play basketball.

Put two words together to make a compound word.
Print the compound word on the line.

1.		sun + flower = _____
2.		rain + coat = _____
3.		wheel + chair = _____
4.		wish + bone = _____
5.		butter + fly = _____

Compound Words

Box 1		
pop	rain	mail
shoe	wheel	back

Box 2		
chair	pack	lace
corn	coat	box

1. mailbox

2.

3.

4.

5.

6.

With your child, see how many compound words you can make using **man, snow, ball, foot,** and **base.**

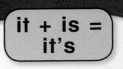

A contraction is a short way of writing two words as one. One or more letters are left out. An apostrophe (') shows where the letters were. **It's** is a contraction. **Look** and **listen** for contractions in the rhyme.

We're waiting for our mom,
she's bringing us a treat.
She's getting it right now—
it's something good to eat.

Write the contraction for the two words in the box.

I am = I'm	she is = she's he is = he's it is = it's	we are = we're you are = you're they are = they're

1. she is	**2.** you are	**3.** it is
4. I am	**5.** we are	**6.** they are

Write a sentence that uses one of the contractions from above.

7. _____

Contractions

he + will =
he'll

is + not =
isn't

Contractions can be made with **will** and **not**.
Write the two words that the contraction stands for.
Look at the words in the box if you need help.

I will = I'll	we will = we'll	is not = isn't
he will = he'll	you will = you'll	do not = don't
she will = she'll	they will = they'll	does not = doesn't
it will = it'll		are not = aren't
		can not = can't

1. I'll	2. aren't	3. you'll
4. don't	5. they'll	6. doesn't
7. isn't	8. we'll	9. can't
10. he'll	11. she'll	12. it'll

PHONICS
ALIVE AT HOME

Read a favorite storybook with your child.
Have him or her point out any contractions
used and tell you what words they stand for.

Spell, Write, and Tell — Say, **spell**, and **talk** about each word in the box. **Print** each word under the correct heading.

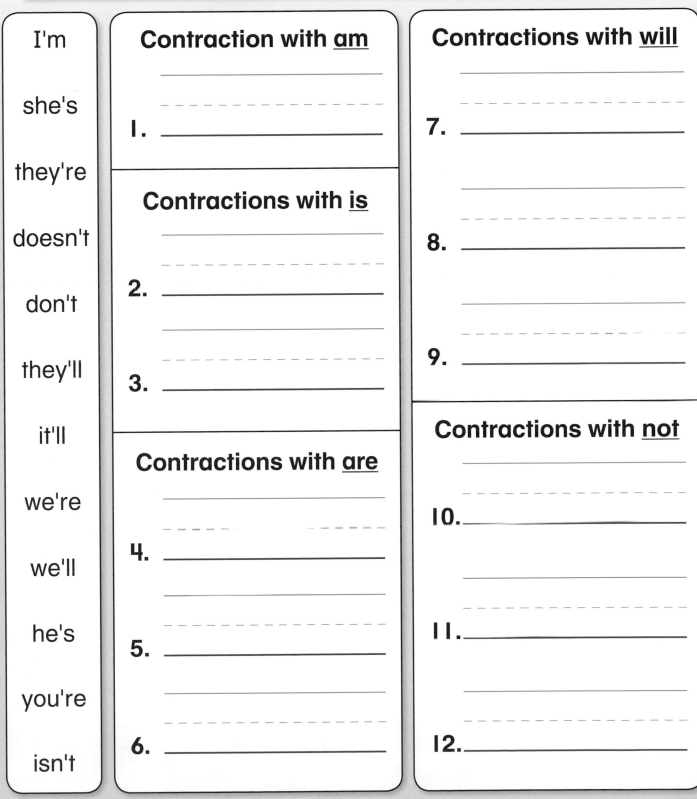

I'm

she's

they're

doesn't

don't

they'll

it'll

we're

we'll

he's

you're

isn't

Contraction with am

1. _____

Contractions with is

2. _____

3. _____

Contractions with are

4. _____

5. _____

6. _____

Contractions with will

7. _____

8. _____

9. _____

Contractions with not

10. _____

11. _____

12. _____

Spell, Write, and Tell

Write about the things your family likes to do in the summer. Use one or more of the words in the box. **Share** what you wrote.

I'm	they're	don't	it'll	we'll	you're
she's	doesn't	they'll	we're	he's	isn't

Things We Do in Summer

PHONICS ALIVE AT HOME Ask your child to draw a picture showing one of the family activities he or she wrote about.

Thinks is made by adding **s** to the end of the root word **think**.
Listen and **look** for words that end in **s** in the rhyme.

"Oh no, rain!" Ann thinks.
But the oak tree smiles.
It drinks and drinks.

Add s to the root word in the box. **Print** the new word on the line.
Read the sentence.

#			
I.		Dad _digs_ in the yard.	dig
2.		Adam _____ the seeds.	plant
3.		Tasha _____ the plants.	water
4.		The garden _____ .	grow
5.		Gram _____ the peas.	pick

Rowing and **rowed** are made by adding **ing** and **ed** to the end of the root word **row**. **Listen** and **look** for words that end in **ing** or **ed** in the rhyme.

Last year Grandpa rowed, but now I am rowing. I'm learning new things because I am growing.

Look at the picture and **read** the root word in Column 1. **Add ing** to the root word in Column 2. **Add ed** to the root word in Column 3.

Column 1 Root Word	Column 2 + ing	Column 3 + ed
1. mix	mixing	mixed
2. kick		
3. yell		
4. crawl		

Help your child add **ing** and **ed** to **walk, look,** and **play.** Then make up sentences using the new words.

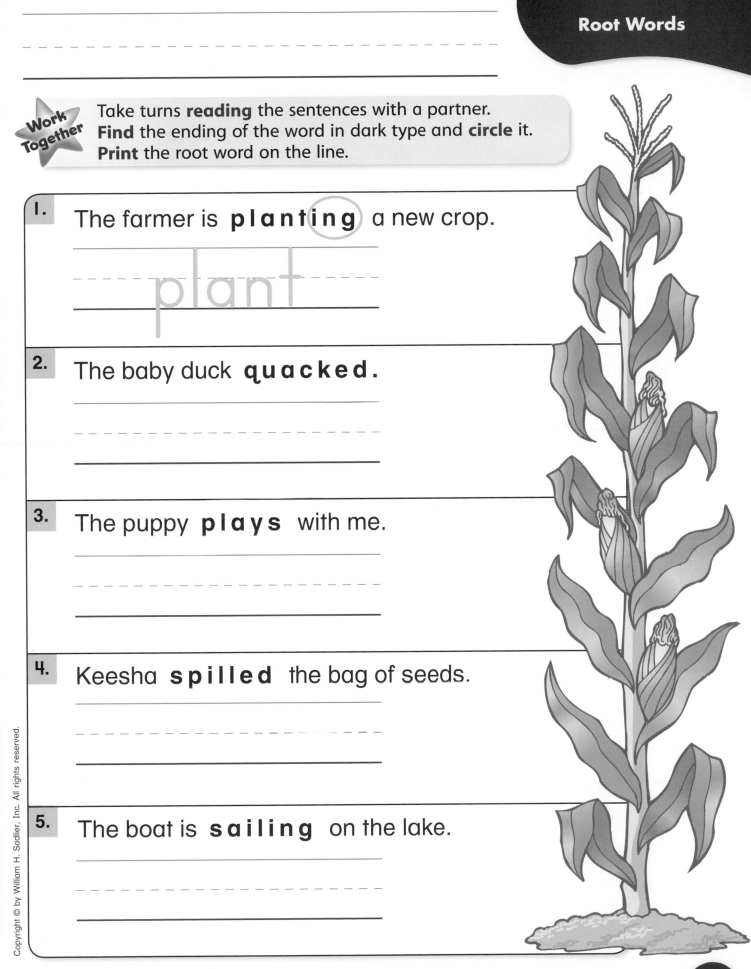

Work Together

Take turns **reading** the sentences with a partner.
Find the ending of the word in dark type and **circle** it.
Print the root word on the line.

1. The farmer is **plant(ing)** a new crop.

plant

2. The baby duck **quacked.**

3. The puppy **plays** with me.

4. Keesha **spilled** the bag of seeds.

5. The boat is **sailing** on the lake.

Read the poem. **Draw** a line under the words that end with **ing** and **ed**. **Write** a complete sentence to answer each question.

Read

Living Things Grow

At first, baby Toyo crawled,
but soon he could walk.
He was playing and laughing
and learning to talk.

All living things grow up,
not just me and you.
Seeds, trees, birds, and pups—
they're all growing, too.

1. How can you tell that something is growing up?

_____

_____

_____

_____

2. What things have you learned since you were a baby?

_____

_____

_____

_____

Lesson 178 • Words with Inflectional Endings
ing and **ed** in Context
Comprehension: Making Generalizations

PHONICS
ALIVE AT HOME

Tell your child what he or she
was like as a baby. Talk about
how your child has grown.

Read Use one of the words in the box to complete each sentence. Practice **reading** the sentences aloud.

| ask | going | he | just | play | up |

1.

"Tim can not walk _____ the 🪜 ," said Tom .

2.

"Tim can not _____ for help yet," said Mom.

3.

"Tim is _____ a 👶 ," said Mom.

4.

"Will Tim _____ 🏏 with me?" asked Tom.

5.

"Will _____ go to the 🛝 with me?" asked Tom.

6.

"Tim is _____ to need you, Tom!" said Mom.

Visit **www.sadlierphonicsonline.com** to do this activity online.

Circle the word in the box that completes each sentence. **Print** the word on the line. **Read** the sentences.

1. I _____ got a pup.	find just
2. He is _____ to be my pal.	ask going
3. I will _____ with him.	play want
4. I will feed and _____ him.	he walk
5. He will grow _____ to be a big dog.	up down

Check-Up   Color a 😊 for each word you wrote.

😊 down   😊 he   😊 want   😊 ask   😊 just

😊 find   😊 going   😊 play   😊 walk   😊 up

326   **Lesson 179** • Reviewing High-Frequency Words

READ

Look at the pictures. **Read** the page.
Talk about what you see.

Learn About Growing

All living things grow.
Sunflowers grow.
So do animals such as tigers.
You're growing, too. Aren't you?

Try matching the young plants
and animals to the older ones.
How are they the same?
How are they different?
How do they change as they grow?

Look at a baby picture of yourself.
Don't you look different now?
How have you changed?

Lesson 180 • Compound Words, Contractions, and Words with Endings in Context
Comprehension: Comparing and Contrasting
Modeling Fluency

Looking Around the Neighborhood

People are walking, talking, and having fun in the neighborhood. **Write** about the picture. Use some words with the endings **s, ed,** and **ing. Look** at the words in the box if you need help.

walks	talking	mailed	crying	jumps
jumping	pulled	helping	playing	rides

PHONICS ALIVE AT HOME   Have your child read the words in the box. Ask him or her to identify the ending used in each word.

Check-Up Make a compound word by **drawing** a line from the first word to another word. **Print** the compound word on the line.

1.

rain coat
wish
sun

_____

2.

pop sticks
corn
robin

_____

3.

mail pen
box
sail

_____

4.

shoe pack
ball
lace

_____

5.

wish bone
nut
wind

_____

6.

wheel news
chair
base

_____

7.

back plane
chair
pack

_____

8.

camp fire
ball
wheel

_____

Check-Up **Circle** the contraction that stands for the underlined words.

1. she is	she'll / she's / isn't
2. I will	we'll / I'll / I'm
3. they will	they'll / they're / I'll
4. they are	aren't / they'll / they're
5. is not	it's / isn't / I'll
6. it will	it'll / it's / I'll

7. do not	don't / doesn't / aren't
8. it is	it's / it'll / we'll
9. are not	isn't / it'll / aren't
10. I am	I'll / I'm / it's
11. we will	we'll / we're / they'll
12. he is	he'll / he's / she's

13. you are	you'll / they'll / you're
14. he will	we're / he's / he'll
15. you will	you're / you'll / he'll
16. she will	she'll / she's / he'll
17. does not	don't / aren't / doesn't
18. we are	we'll / you're / we're

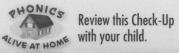

PHONICS ALIVE AT HOME Review this Check-Up with your child.

⭐ **Check-Up** **Circle** the word that completes the sentence. **Print** the word on the line.

1. It is _____ on my hat!	rain rained raining
2. I _____ for Sam to come home.	yells yelled yelling
3. The man _____ here for the bus.	wait waits waiting
4. Dad is _____ the grass.	mows mowed mowing
5. Jim _____ Sue bake a cake.	help helped helping
6. That boat _____ on the lake.	sail sails sailing

Check-Up **Circle** the word that completes the sentence.
Print the word on the line.

1.

The dog is _____ up on me.

jumps
jumped
jumping

2.

I _____ to play with the cat.

wants
wanted
wanting

3.

Dad _____ the flute.

play
plays
playing

4.

I am _____ you a big box.

mail
mailed
mailing

5.

Jill _____ home with Tom.

walk
walks
walking

6.

Mom _____ the pot to the top.

fill
filled
filling

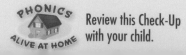

PHONICS ALIVE AT HOME Review this Check-Up with your child.

Growing Up

Name _____

Reading at Home: Read the book together. Talk about how a caterpillar and a butterfly are alike and different. Then find compound words, contractions, and words with **s** and **ing** endings in the story.

It starts eating and eating.

Growing up looks pretty good, don't you think?

Doesn't the bug's new home look funny?

DIRECTIONS: Cut and fold the book.

Lesson 184 • Unit 6 Take-Home Book
Comprehension: Comparing
and Contrasting

4

Someday this little bug is going to be a butterfly.

It grows bigger every day.

Fold

Fold

Then it hangs upside down.

Soon the butterfly comes out.

5

My Progress Checklist

😒 I need to practice this.   🙂 I know this.

Unit 1: Consonants

○ 🙂 f	○ 🙂 g	○ 🙂 x
○ 🙂 m	○ 🙂 w	○ 🙂 ff
○ 🙂 s	○ 🙂 p	○ 🙂 ss
○ 🙂 t	○ 🙂 r	○ 🙂 tt
○ 🙂 h	○ 🙂 k	○ 🙂 ll
○ 🙂 b	○ 🙂 j	○ 🙂 dd
○ 🙂 l	○ 🙂 q(u)	○ 🙂 gg
○ 🙂 d	○ 🙂 v	○ 🙂 zz
○ 🙂 c	○ 🙂 y	
○ 🙂 n	○ 🙂 z	

Unit 2: Short Vowels

○ 🙂 a
○ 🙂 i
○ 🙂 o
○ 🙂 u
○ 🙂 e

Unit 3: Long Vowels

○ 🙂 a
○ 🙂 i
○ 🙂 o
○ 🙂 u
○ 🙂 e

Unit 4: Consonant Blends

○ ☺ l blends
○ ☺ r blends
○ ☺ s blends
○ ☺ blends at the
  end of words

Unit 5: Consonant Digraphs

○ ☺ th
○ ☺ sh
○ ☺ wh
○ ☺ ch
○ ☺ ck

High-Frequency Words

○ ☺ by
○ ☺ funny
○ ☺ let
○ ☺ ride
○ ☺ stop
○ ☺ walk

○ ☺ and
○ ☺ help
○ ☺ it
○ ☺ no
○ ☺ see
○ ☺ will

○ ☺ down
○ ☺ how
○ ☺ little
○ ☺ please

Unit 6: Word Structure

○ ☺ compound words
○ ☺ contractions
○ ☺ endings **s, ing, ed**

○ ☺ put
○ ☺ said

○ ☺ again
○ ☺ ate
○ ☺ big
○ ☺ look
○ ☺ to
○ ☺ yellow

○ ☺ come
○ ☺ find

○ ☺ open
○ ☺ out
○ ☺ want
○ ☺ we

○ ☺ ask
○ ☺ going
○ ☺ he
○ ☺ just
○ ☺ play
○ ☺ up